SMALL ENGINES

Third Edition

Workbook

BRIGGS & STRATTON

Authorized by
Briggs & Stratton Corporation

Equipment & Engine
Training Council

AMERICAN TECHNICAL PUBLISHERS, INC.
HOMEWOOD, ILLINOIS 60430-4600

R. Bruce Radcliff

Cobalite and Vanguard are trademarks of Briggs & Stratton Corporation. Magnetron is a registered trademark of Briggs & Stratton Corporation. DU is a registered trademark of GGB North America.

3 4 5 6 7 8 9 – 09 – 9 8 7 6 5 4 3 2 1

Printed in the United States of America

ISBN 978-0-8269-0027-2

 This book is printed on 30% recycled paper.

TABLE OF CONTENTS

INTRODUCTION

Small Engines Workbook is designed for use with *Small Engines*. This workbook contains two tests per chapter (Test 1 and Test 2) based on the content of each chapter and a Final Exam based on Chapters 1–12.

These tests are primarily objective in nature, and consist of completion, multiple choice, true-false, and identification questions.

MST Sample Exam questions are provided for each chapter in *Small Engines*. These questions are similar in content and format to the questions in *Master Service Technician Exam* administered by Briggs & Stratton.

Answers to problems in this workbook are rounded to the nearest tenths (0.0) for %, lb/in., and ft.; to the nearest thousandths (0.000) for in. and kW; and to the nearest hundredths (0.00) for all other units unless otherwise noted. When selecting motors, round up to the next higher 0.5 HP. Answers to all problems (and solutions as appropriate) are given in *Small Engines Workbook Answer Key*.

The Publisher

TEST 1
INTERNAL COMBUSTION ENGINES

CHAPTER

Name _____ Date _____

T   F   **1.** An engine is a machine that converts a form of energy into mechanical force.

_____   **2.** Small engines are generally rated up to ___ HP.
    A. 20
    B. 25
    C. 30
    D. none of the above

T   F   **3.** Horizontally opposed engines have a low profile and produce a low degree of vibration.

_____   **4.** Approximately ___% of the energy released when fuel is oxidized in a typical small engine is converted into useful work.

T   F   **5.** Heat is the resource that provides the capacity to do work.

T   F   **6.** Gasoline or any other fossil fuel has potential energy based on its chemical state.

T   F   **7.** A substance can be in solid, liquid, or gas state.

_____   **8.** Three methods of heat transfer are ___.
    A. conduction, convection, and locomotion
    B. conduction, radiation, and locomotion
    C. conduction, convection, and radiation
    D. none of the above

_____   **9.** A(n) ___ is the amount of heat energy required to raise the temperature of 1 lb of water 1°F.

_____   **10.** A(n) ___ is the amount of heat energy required to change the temperature of 1 g of water 1°C.

_____   **11.** ___ is heat transfer that occurs when heat is transferred by currents in a fluid.

_____   **12.** When degrees Fahrenheit is known, degrees Celsius is found by applying the formula ___.
    A. $°C = \dfrac{°F + 32}{1.8}$

    B. $°C = \dfrac{°F - 32}{1.8}$

    C. $°C = \dfrac{1.8}{°F + 32}$

    D. $°C = \dfrac{1.8}{°F - 32}$

_____   **13.** ___ is the number of unit squares equal to the surface of an object.

1

_____ **14.** Force is measured in ___ in the English system.

_____ **15.** When force and area are known, pressure is found by applying the formula ___.

      A. $P = F \times A$

      B. $P = \dfrac{A}{F}$

      C. $P = F + A$

      D. $P = \dfrac{F}{A}$

_____ **16.** ___ is a force acting on a perpendicular radial distance from a point of rotation.

_____ **17.** A(n) ___ is a simple machine that consists of a rigid bar which pivots on a fulcrum with both resistance and effort applied.

_____ **18.** The ___ is the measurement from the center of the crankshaft to the center of the crankpin journal, which is used to determine the stroke of an engine.

_____ **19.** ___ occurs only when force results in motion.

_____ **20.** Horsepower is a unit of power equal to ___.

      A. 746 W

      B. 33,000 lb-ft/min

      C. 746 W or 33,000 lb-ft/min

      D. none of the above

_____ **21.** When force and distance are known, work is found by applying the formula ___.

      A. $W = F \times D$

      B. $W = F - D$

      C. $W = F + D$

      D. none of the above

T   F   **22.** Both four-stroke cycle and two-stroke cycle engines complete four distinct events during each cycle.

T   F   **23.** Small engines are either air-cooled or liquid-cooled.

_____ **24.** When heat is added to water, it changes to ___.

_____ **25.** A(n) ___ is a multi-channeled container that allows air to pass around the channels to remove heat from the liquid within.

_____ **26.** Water boils at ___°F.

_____ **27.** One horsepower equals ___ lb-ft per sec.

T   F   **28.** Walk-behind lawn mowers are conservatively estimated to have an average useful life of 12 years.

T   F   **29.** The MST exam must be completed during a 4½ hour period.

T   F   **30.** Generators and snow throwers commonly use a vertical shaft, horizontal cylinder engine.

Temperature

_____ **1.** The temperature at A equals ___°C.

_____ **2.** The temperature at B equals ___°C.

_____ **3.** The temperature at C equals ___°F.

_____ **4.** The temperature at D equals ___°F.

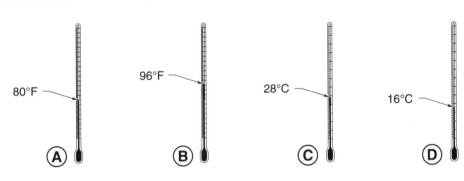

Horsepower

_____ **1.** The horsepower rating of Engine A is ___ HP.

_____ **2.** The horsepower rating of Engine B is ___ HP.

_____ **3.** The horsepower rating of Engine C is ___ HP.

_____ **4.** The horsepower rating of Engine D is ___ HP.

| 412,500 lb-ft | 360,000 lb-ft | 564,000 lb-ft | 550,000 lb-ft |
| A | B | C | D |

Two-Stroke

_____ **1.** The stroke shown at A is the ___ stroke.

_____ **2.** The stroke shown at B is the ___ stroke.

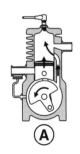
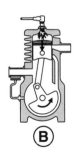

Four-Stroke

_____ **1.** The stroke shown at A is the ___ stroke.

_____ **2.** The stroke shown at B is the ___ stroke.

_____ **3.** The stroke shown at C is the ___ stroke.

_____ **4.** The stroke shown at D is the ___ stroke.

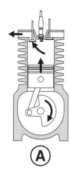 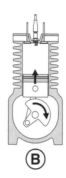 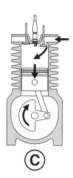 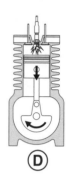

Cylinder Design

_____ **1.** The cylinder design at A is ___.

_____ **2.** The cylinder design at B is ___.

_____ **3.** The cylinder design at C is ___.

_____ **4.** The cylinder design at D is ___.

_____ **5.** The cylinder design at E is ___.

_____ **6.** The cylinder design at F is ___.

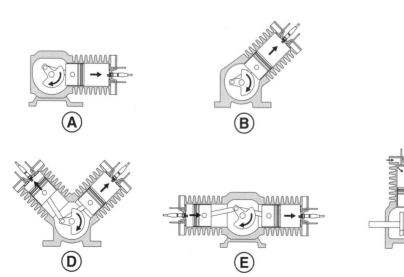

Name _____   Date _____

_____ **1.** An external combustion engine generates heat energy from the combustion of a fuel ___ the engine.

  A. inside
  B. outside
  C. inside or outside
  D. none of the above

_____ **2.** Most walk-behind rotary lawn mowers use a ___ shaft, ___ cylinder engine.

  A. vertical; vertical
  B. horizontal; horizontal
  C. vertical; horizontal
  D. horizontal; vertical

_____ **3.** The first 50,000,000 Briggs & Stratton engines were produced between 1924 and ___.

_____ **4.** The first successful gasoline engine was developed by ___.

  A. Thomas Savery
  B. Eugene Lebon
  C. James Watt
  D. none of the above

T   F   **5.** Kinetic energy is energy of motion.

T   F   **6.** Heat is kinetic energy.

T   F   **7.** Heat is always transferred from a substance with a lower temperature to a substance with a higher temperature.

_____ **8.** ___ is the measurement of the degree or intensity of heat.

_____ **9.** A Btu is the amount of heat energy required to raise the temperature of ___ lb of water ___°F.

  A. 0.746; 1
  B. 1; 1
  C. 1; 0.746
  D. none of the above

_____ **10.** A calorie is the amount of heat energy required to change the temperature of 1 ___ of water 1°C.

_____ **11.** ___ is heat transfer that occurs as radiant energy without a material carrier.

_____ **12.** When degrees Celsius is known, degrees Fahrenheit is found by applying the formula ___.

  A. $°F = (1.8 + °C) + 32$
  B. $°F = (°C - 1.8) + 32$
  C. $°F = (1.8 \times °C) + 32$
  D. $°F = (1.8 + °C) - 32$

5

_____ **13.** ___ is a force acting on a unit of area.

_____ **14.** Force is measured in ___ in the SI metric system.

_____ **15.** A(n) ___, when referring to force, is anything with mass.

_____ **16.** When force and radius (distance) are known, torque is found by applying the formula ___.
  A. $T = F \times r$
  B. $T = F - r$
  C. $T = F + r$
  D. none of the above

_____ **17.** The ___ is the linear distance a piston travels inside the cylinder.

_____ **18.** ___ is the movement of an object by a constant force to a specific distance.

_____ **19.** ___ is the rate at which work is done.

_____ **20.** Horsepower is found by applying the formula ___.
  A. $HP = \dfrac{W \times T}{33,000}$

  B. $HP = \dfrac{W}{T \times 33,000}$

  C. $HP = \dfrac{W - T}{33,000}$

  D. $HP = \dfrac{T}{W} \times 33,000$

T F **21.** Small engines are either spark ignition or compression ignition based on how the fuel is ignited.

T F **22.** Shaft orientation is axis of the crankshaft as vertical or horizontal.

_____ **23.** When heat is added to ice, it changes to ___.

_____ **24.** Heat flows from one substance to another when a(n) ___ difference exists.

_____ **25.** A glass ___ is a graduated glass tube that is filled with a material such as alcohol or mercury which expands when heated and contracts when cooled.

_____ **26.** Water boils at ___°C.

T F **27.** All internal combustion engines utilize some form of fossil fuel as a source of energy.

T F **28.** The size of lawn tractor engines commonly ranges from 11 HP to 18 HP.

T F **29.** The MST exam consists of over 500 questions.

T F **30.** Potential energy is stored energy a body has due to its position, chemical state, or condition.

Work

_____ **1.** The work produced at A is ___ lb-ft.

_____ **2.** The work produced at B is ___ lb-ft.

_____ **3.** The work produced at C is ___ lb-ft.

_____ **4.** The work produced at D is ___ lb-ft.

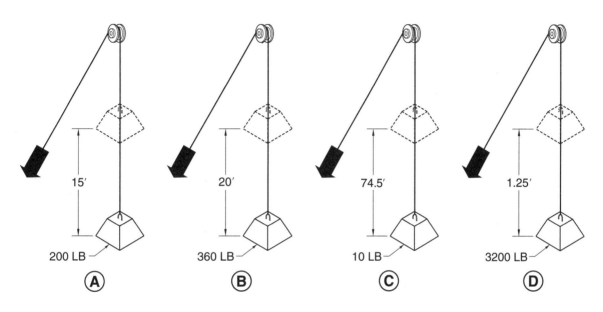

Cooling System

_____ **1.** The cooling system at A is ___-cooled.

_____ **2.** The cooling system at B is ___-cooled.

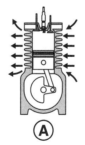
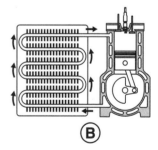

Shaft Orientation

_____ **1.** The shaft orientation at A is ___.

_____ **2.** The shaft orientation at B is ___.

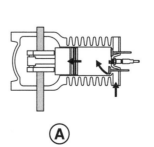
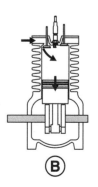

Torque

_____ **1.** The torque produced at A is ___ lb-ft.

_____ **2.** The torque produced at B is ___ lb-ft.

_____ **3.** The torque produced at C is ___ lb-ft.

_____ **4.** The torque produced at D is ___ lb-ft.

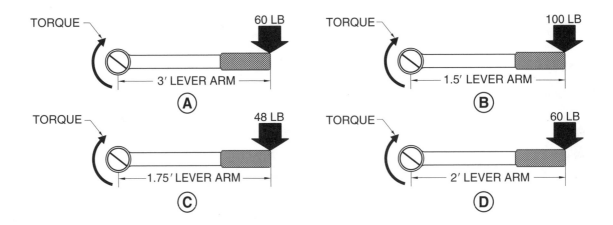

Heat

_____ **1.** The method of heat transfer at A is ___.

_____ **2.** The method of heat transfer at B is ___.

_____ **3.** The method of heat transfer at C is ___.

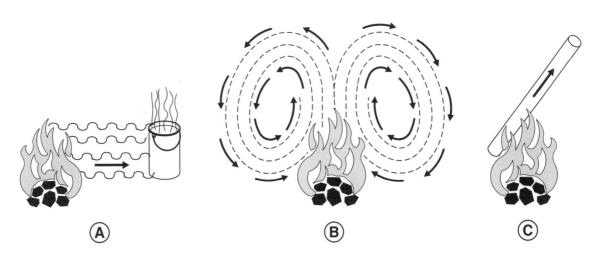

Name _____   Date _____

1. Why is heated liquid coolant pumped through the upper inlet of the radiator instead of the lower inlet of the radiator?

   A. Because the pump rotates clockwise, causing the discharge to be located at the highest point on the pump housing.

   B. Because the hot liquid coolant will always rise to the top of the pump housing.

   C. To allow easier servicing of the cooling system.

   D. As the cooling liquid temperature decreases in the radiator, the cooler liquid will collect at the bottom to be reused by the cooling system.

2. All other things being equal (compression ratio, volume of fuel, air, etc.), can the downward force or pressure on a piston be increased by using a domed piston head configuration?

   Yes

   No

3. The addition of a ⅜″ × 6″ extension to a ⅜″ drive torque wrench will increase the torque value at a fastener by 50%.

   True

   False

4. A 55 gal. drum of engine oil needs to be moved from the level of the parking lot to the back of a pick-up truck. The bed of the truck is 3′ above the flat surface of the parking lot. The drum of oil weighs 500 lb. Based on the equation for work ($W = F \times D$), 1500 ft/lbs of work will accomplish the task.

   Technician A says that less work is done by rolling the drum up a 6′ long ramp into the truck than by lifting the oil drum into the truck bed.

   Technician B says that the amount of work remains the same if the drum were lifted into the truck, but the effort exerted by the person rolling the drum would be decreased.

   Which technician is correct?

   A. Technician A

   B. Technician B

   C. Both Technicians A and B

   D. Neither Technicians A nor B

9

5. If gasoline and atmospheric air are combined and oxidized in the perfect ratio, what new compounds are created?

    A. Oxygen and nitrogen

    B. Carbon dioxide and water

    C. Carbon monoxide and water

    D. Oxides of nitrogen and carbon dioxide

Name _____ Date _____

_____ 1. The Occupational Safety and Health Administration is a federal agency that requires all employers to provide a(n) ___ environment for their employees.
A. safe
B. inviting
C. contemporary
D. none of the above

T   F   2. NIOSH is primarily concerned with research activities, while OSHA is responsible for enforcement.

T   F   3. The DOD is responsible for developing Mil Standards.

_____ 4. The ___ is the federal agency which controls and abates pollution for air, water, solid waste, pesticides, radiation, and toxic substances.
A. CPSC
B. SAE
C. ASTM
D. none of the above

_____ 5. The maximum blade tip speed for rotary lawn equipment is ___ fpm.
A. 14,000
B. 19,000
C. 23,500
D. 25,000

_____ 6. A(n) ___ is a regulation or minimum requirement.

_____ 7. The American National Standards Institute is a national organization that ___.
A. helps identify needs for national standards
B. is the national coordinator of voluntary standards activities
C. all of the above
D. none of the above

_____ 8. Technical ___ are organizations composed of groups of engineers and technical personnel united by professional interest.

_____ 9. The United States representative to ISO is ___.

_____ 10. The ___ is the largest organization in the world devoted to developing and publishing voluntary, full-consensus standards.

T   F   11. UL® is a government organization that tests equipment and products to verify conformance to national codes and standards.

T   F   12. The NFPA publishes the *National Electrical Code®*.

11

T F **13.** Trade associations are organizations that represent producers and distributors of specific products.

_____ **14.** To start and sustain a fire, ___ must be present.
    A. fuel
    B. heat
    C. oxygen
    D. all of the above

T F **15.** Fire extinguishers are designed for one or more classes of fire.

_____ **16.** A(n) ___ liquid is a liquid that has a flash point below 100°F.

_____ **17.** A UL®-approved safety can shall not exceed ___ gal.

_____ **18.** Vapor pressure is the pressure exerted by vapor above the ___ of a liquid in a closed container.

T F **19.** The labeling on safety cans must comply with NFPA standards.

_____ **20.** Carbon monoxide is ___.
    A. toxic
    B. odorless
    C. tasteless
    D. all of the above

T F **21.** Carbon monoxide is slightly heavier than air.

T F **22.** Goggles with colored lenses provide protection from UV rays produced by welding equipment.

_____ **23.** A(n) ___ material is any material capable of posing a risk to health, safety, and property.

_____ **24.** ___ tools are tools that are powered by hand.

_____ **25.** A(n) ___ hazard is the degree of susceptibility of materials to burning based on the form or condition of the material and its surrounding environment.

_____ **26.** A(n) ___ plan is a document that details the exact action to be taken in the event of an emergency.

_____ **27.** A(n) ___ tool is a measurement tool used to test the condition or operation of an engine component or system.

T F **28.** Cutting tools should be pointed away from the body during use.

T F **29.** A reactivity hazard is the degree of susceptibility of materials to release energy by themselves or by exposure to certain conditions or substances.

T F **30.** Electrical tools should not be used in a wet or damp area.

Tools

_____   **1.** The tool at ___ is used to mark the centerpoint for drilling a hole.

_____   **2.** The tool at ___ is used to drive fasteners, shafts, and bearings.

_____   **3.** The tool at ___ is used to measure electrical values.

_____   **4.** The tool at ___ is used to remove flywheels.

_____   **5.** The tool at ___ is used to compress piston rings for installation.

_____   **6.** The tool at ___ is used to install and remove snap ring fasteners.

_____   **7.** The tool at ___ is used to cut external threads.

_____   **8.** The tool at ___ is used to form and/or smooth material.

_____   **9.** The tool at ___ is used to measure thickness and diameter.

_____ **10.** The tool at ___ is used to measure engine speed in rpm.

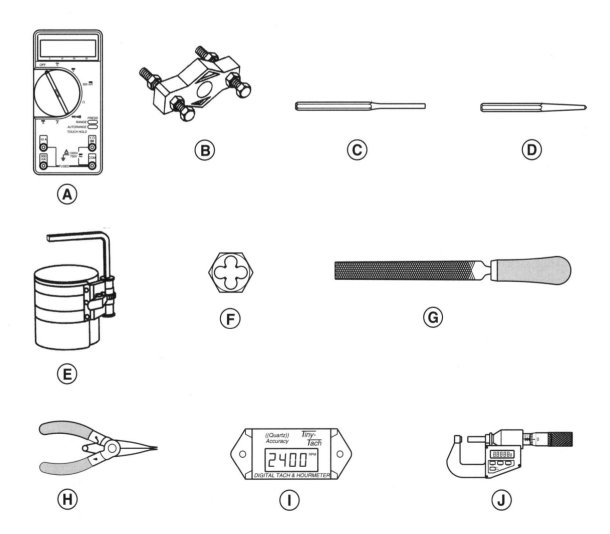

Hazardous Material Container Labeling

_____ **1.** A indicates a(n) ___ hazard.

_____ **2.** B indicates ___.

_____ **3.** C indicates a(n) ___ hazard.

_____ **4.** D indicates a(n) ___ hazard.

Safety Color Coding

_____ **1.** Designate(s) traffic and housekeeping areas.

_____ **2.** Designate(s) caution.

_____ **3.** Designate(s) radiation.

_____ **4.** Designate(s) safety and location of first aid equipment.

_____ **5.** Designate(s) danger and stop.

_____ **6.** Designate(s) dangerous parts of machines.

RED	YELLOW	ORANGE	BLACK, WHITE, OR B/W	GREEN	PURPLE
Ⓐ	Ⓑ	Ⓒ	Ⓓ	Ⓔ	Ⓕ

Fire Extinguisher Classes

_____ **1.** The class of fire at A is ___.

_____ **2.** The class of fire at B is ___.

_____ **3.** The class of fire at C is ___.

_____ **4.** The class of fire at D is ___.

Ⓐ

Ⓑ

Ⓒ

Ⓓ

Name _____   Date _____

_____ **1.** OSHA was established under the Occupational Safety and Health Act of ___.
  A. 1964
  B. 1970
  C. 1976
  D. 1982

T   F   **2.** NIOSH has established a color code to designate certain cautions and dangers in work areas.

T   F   **3.** The federal agency responsible for traffic control is the DOT.

_____ **4.** Rotary lawn equipment blades must stop within ___ sec of leaving the operator presence zone.
  A. 3
  B. 5
  C. 6
  D. none of the above

_____ **5.** Government agencies are ___ government organizations and departments which establish rules and regulations related to safety, health, and equipment installation and operation.
  A. federal
  B. state
  C. local
  D. all of the above

_____ **6.** A(n) ___ is an accepted reference or practice.

_____ **7.** The ___ is a nongovernmental international organization comprised of national standards institutions of over 90 countries.
  A. IIO
  B. ISO
  C. OIS
  D. SOI

_____ **8.** The ___ provides standards used in industry for the manufacture of agricultural equipment.

_____ **9.** The ___ promotes the engineering advancement of mobile systems.

_____ **10.** The ___ is a Canadian national organization that develops standards and provides facilities for certification testing to national and international standards.

T   F   **11.** The Equipment and Engine Training Council (EETC) promotes and supports the education and training of small engine service technicians.

T   F   **12.** The NFPA is a national organization that develops mechanical testing standards.

15

_____ **13.** The ___ is the national trade association representing manufacturers of consumer and commercial outdoor power equipment and their major components.

    A. IPEO

    B. OPEI

    C. IOPE

    D. none of the above

_____ **14.** The number and type of fire extinguishers required are determined by the ___.

T   F   **15.** State and local codes may require a scheduled inspection of fire extinguishers.

_____ **16.** A(n) ___ liquid is a liquid that has a flash point at or above 100°F.

_____ **17.** ___ is the use of metal-to-metal contact or a wire between two containers to prevent possible ignition from static electricity sparks.

_____ **18.** ___ combustion is self-ignition caused by chemical reaction and temperature buildup in waste material.

T   F   **19.** The lid of an oily waste can must remain open to prevent ignition of contained materials.

_____ **20.** Air normally contains ___% oxygen.

    A. 10

    B. 15

    C. 21

    D. 26

T   F   **21.** Protective clothing should be loose.

_____ **22.** A chemical ___ is a solid, liquid, gas, mist, dust, and/or vapor that is toxic when inhaled, absorbed, or ingested.

_____ **23.** A(n) ___ is printed material used to relay hazardous material information from the manufacturer, importer, or distributor to employer and employees.

_____ **24.** A(n) ___ report is a document that details facts about an accident in the facility.

_____ **25.** A(n) ___ hazard is any extraordinary properties and hazards associated with a particular material.

_____ **26.** Power tools are tools that are ___ powered.

    A. electrically

    B. pneumatically

    C. hydraulically

    D. all of the above

T   F   **27.** Tools should not be carried in a pocket.

T   F   **28.** All injuries should be reported to a supervisor.

T   F   **29.** Fasteners should be removed by pushing the tool toward the body.

T   F   **30.** Stand to one side when starting and using a grinder.

Tools

_____ **1.** The tool at ___ is used to cut internal threads in predrilled holes.

_____ **2.** The tool at ___ is used to cut wire and other material.

_____ **3.** The tool at ___ is used to verify distance between parts.

_____ **4.** The tool at ___ is used to measure inside, outside, and depth of parts.

_____ **5.** The tool at ___ is used to loosen/tighten hex screws.

_____ **6.** The tool at ___ is used to test sealing capability of compression components.

_____ **7.** The tool at ___ is used to remove and torque the rewind starter clutch.

_____ **8.** The tool at ___ is used to measure change in position of parts.

_____ **9.** The tool at ___ is used to test the condition of the ignition system.

_____ **10.** The tool at ___ is used to transfer distance from parts to measurement tool.

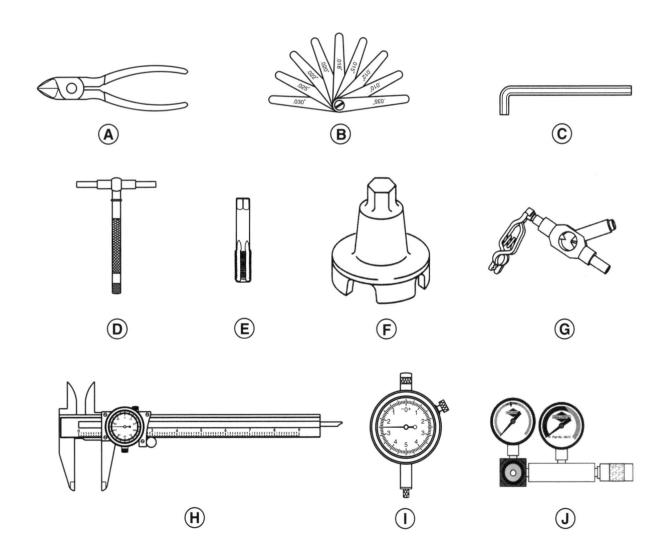

Sound Levels

_____ **1.** The sound is barely audible.

_____ **2.** The sound is very quiet.

_____ **3.** The sound is moderate.

_____ **4.** The sound is noisy.

_____ **5.** The sound is deafening.

60 db   **90 db**   **10 db**
Ⓐ   Ⓑ   Ⓒ

140 db   **30 db**
Ⓓ   Ⓔ

Digital Multimeter Tests

_____ **1.** The test at A is a(n) ___ test.

_____ **2.** The test at B is a(n) ___ test.

_____ **3.** The test at C is a(n) ___ test.

_____ **4.** The test at D is a(n) ___ test.

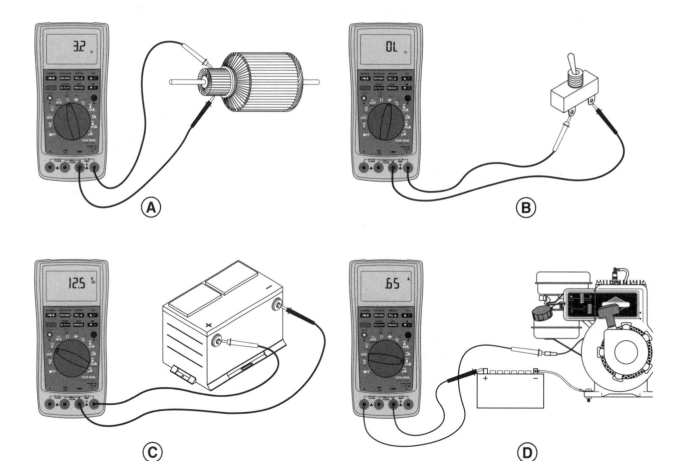

Name _____   Date _____

1. The CPSC standard for blade stopping time and blade tip speed is ___.

   A. 3.5 seconds/16,000 ft per minute

   B. 3.5 seconds/19,000 ft per minute

   C. 3 seconds/16,000 ft per minute

   D. 3 seconds/19,000 ft per minute

2. The American Petroleum Institute (API) sets standards for the viscosity of all engine oils.

   True
   False

3. Carbon monoxide (CO) is lighter than air and may accumulate almost anywhere in a closed workshop.

   True
   False

4. An MSDS is a printed informational sheet pertaining to various materials a small engine service technician may encounter while performing engine service. Which of the following subjects are found on an MSDS?

   A. Health hazards

   B. Flammability hazards

   C. Spill or leak procedures

   D. all of the above

5. A cylinder leakdown tester is used by a small engine service technician to determine the sealing capabilities of an engine. The most important component of successful and accurate testing is to:

   A. Make sure the engine displacement is larger than 13 cubic inches.

   B. Remove the muffler and carburetor before testing.

   C. Listen carefully to all external orifices for audible leaks.

   D. Test the air flow through the leakdown tester before attaching to the engine.

6. The proper method for testing for spark in a Briggs & Stratton engine is to:

    A. Remove the spark plug, connect the spark plug lead, lay the base of the spark plug against any good engine ground, and rotate the engine a minimum of 350 rpm.

    B. Remove the spark plug, hold the spark plug lead ¼″ away from the engine block, and rotate the engine a minimum of 350 rpm.

    C. Remove the spark plug, install the spark tester, and rotate the engine a minimum of 350 rpm.

    D. Remove the spark plug lead, hold it ¼″ away from the end of the spark plug, and observe the color and sound of the spark when the engine is rotated.

Name _____   Date _____

_____ **1.** The ___ is the main structure of an engine which supports and helps maintain alignment of internal and external components.

_____ **2.** The ___ of an engine is the linear distance that a piston travels in the cylinder bore from top dead center to bottom dead center.

_____ **3.** The ___ of an engine is the diameter of the cylinder bore.

T   F   **4.** Internal combustion engines convert potential chemical energy in the form of heat derived from a fuel into mechanical energy.

_____ **5.** ___ is the point at which the piston is farthest from the cylinder head.
   A. TDC
   B. BDC
   C. MDC
   D. none of the above

_____ **6.** The atmospheric pressure at sea level is ___ psi.
   A. 0.147
   B. 1.47
   C. 14.7
   D. 147

_____ **7.** A(n) ___ is an engine component that houses and supports the crankshaft.

_____ **8.** The ___ is a removable part of the engine crankcase that serves as an oil reservoir and provides access to internal parts.

_____ **9.** A(n) ___ is the filler material placed between the cylinder block and cylinder head to seal the combustion chamber.

_____ **10.** A(n) ___ engine is an engine that has valves and related components located in the cylinder head.

T   F   **11.** Head gaskets are made from hard metals and graphite layered together.

T   F   **12.** Cast iron cylinder blocks are heavier and more expensive, but are more resistant to wear and less prone to heat distortion than cast aluminum alloy cylinder blocks.

T   F   **13.** All engine blocks are produced as one-piece units.

_____ **14.** The ___ is the measurement from the center of the crankshaft to the center of the crankpin journal, which is used to determine the stroke of an engine.

_____ **15.** A(n) ___ journal is a precision ground surface within which the crankshaft rotates.

_____ **16.** The ___ is a gear located on the crankshaft that is used to drive other parts of an engine.

_____ **17.** A(n) ___ is a cylindrical engine component that slides back and forth in the cylinder bore by forces produced during the combustion process.

_____ **18.** The ___ of a piston is the portion of the piston closest to the crankshaft that helps align the piston as it moves in the cylinder bore.

T F   **19.** Piston rings are commonly made from cast iron.

_____ **20.** A(n) ___ is an engine component that transfers motion from the piston to the crankshaft and functions as a lever arm.

_____ **21.** A(n) ___ is the removable section of a two-piece connecting rod that provides a bearing surface for the crankpin journal.

T F   **22.** A radial load is a load applied parallel to the shaft.

T F   **23.** A rod bearing provides a low-friction pivot point between the connecting rod and the crankshaft and the connecting rod and piston.

T F   **24.** Diesel fuel is rated by octane number.

_____ **25.** ___ is the property of matter by which any physical body persists in its state of rest or uniform motion until acted upon by an external force.
  A. Tension
  B. Inertia
  C. Balance
  D. none of the above

_____ **26.** The ___ is the volume of compressed air-fuel mixture trapped inside the combustion chamber ready for ignition.

_____ **27.** The compression ratio of an engine is a comparison of the volume of the combustion chamber with the piston at ___ to the volume of the combustion chamber with the piston at ___.
  A. BDC; TDC
  B. TDC; BDC
  C. BDC; MDC
  D. MDC; BDC

_____ **28.** The ___ event is an engine operation event in which hot expanding gases force the piston head away from the cylinder head.

_____ **29.** Valve ___ is the period during engine operation when both intake and exhaust valves are open at the same time.

_____ **30.** The valve ___ is the machine surface of a valve that mates with the valve seat to seal the combustion chamber.

_____ **31.** On four-stroke cycle engines, the camshaft rotates at ___ the speed of the crankshaft.
  A. ¼
  B. ½
  C. twice
  D. none of the above

_____ **32.** A(n) ___ is a diesel engine component that preheats air inside the combustion chamber to facilitate ignition of the charge.

_____ **33.** ___ horsepower, or shaft horsepower, is the amount of usable power taken from an engine.

_____ **34.** The ___ dynamometer is a dynamometer used to measure engine torque using a brake that exerts pressure on a spring scale.

_____ **35.** ___ efficiency is a measurement that compares the amount of chemical energy available in fuel converted into heat energy used to produce useful work.

T　　F **36.** The larger the displacement of an engine, the less power it produces.

_____ **37.** Piston rings are commonly made from ___.
　　A. aluminum
　　B. babbitt
　　C. cast iron
　　D. stainless steel

T　　F **38.** An oil ring is the piston ring with a tapered face located in the ring groove between the compression ring and oil ring.

_____ **39.** A(n) ___ is the bearing surface in an antifriction bearing that supports rolling elements during rotation.

_____ **40.** Diesel engines commonly have a compression ratio ranging from ___:1 to ___:1.
　　A. 6; 8.5
　　B. 10; 30
　　C. 14; 25
　　D. 15; 35

T　　F **41.** Turbo lag is the measurement of air pressure generated by the turbocharger that exceeds ambient air pressure.

_____ **42.** ___ is a chemical process used to produce biodiesel fuel, where glycerin is separated from fat or vegetable oil.

_____ **43.** A(n) ___ is an engine component that is designed to improve engine performance through the introduction of additional air into the intake system.
　　A. air filter
　　B. catalytic converter
　　C. muffler
　　D. turbocharger

T　　F **44.** Biodiesel fuel contains no petroleum, but can be blended at any level with petroleum diesel to create a biodiesel blend.

_____ **45.** A(n) ___ is a component that provides a turbocharger with the needed rotational force to compress ambient air to a positive pressure.

_____ **46.** A ___ bearing provides support and a low-friction bearing surface for the crankshaft.
　　A. ball
　　B. main
　　C. needle
　　D. rod

T   F   **47.** Valve overlap designed into an engine is most useful at lower speeds.

_____   **48.** A(n) ___ is the top surface of the piston, which is subjected to tremendous forces and heat during normal operation.

T   F   **49.** An antifriction bearing contains moving elements to provide a low-friction support surface for rotating or sliding surfaces.

_____   **50.** Piston rings commonly used on small engines include the compression ring, wiper ring, and ___ ring.
  A. combustion
  B. cylinder
  C. oil
  D. seal

Displacement

_____   **1.** The displacement of the single cylinder engine at A is ___ cu in.

_____   **2.** The displacement of the single cylinder engine at B is ___ cu in.

_____   **3.** The displacement of the single cylinder engine at C is ___ cu in.

_____   **4.** The displacement of the single cylinder engine at D is ___ cu in.

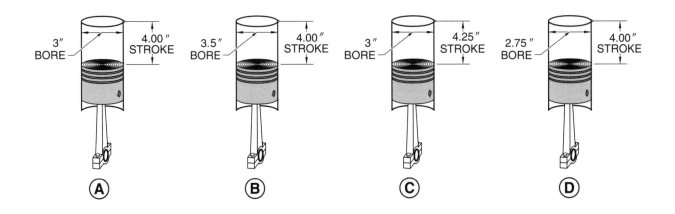

Diesels

_____ **1.** The piston is shown at ___.

_____ **2.** The precombustion chamber is shown at ___.

_____ **3.** The cylinder head is shown at ___.

_____ **4.** The cylinder block is shown at ___.

_____ **5.** The injector is shown at ___.

_____ **6.** The glow plug is shown at ___.

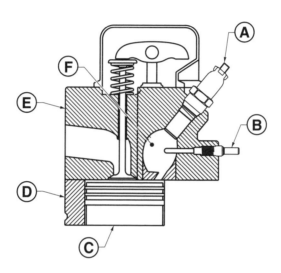

Connecting Rod

_____ **1.** The piston pin is shown at ___.

_____ **2.** The rod cap is shown at ___.

_____ **3.** The connecting rod is shown at ___.

_____ **4.** The piston is shown at ___.

_____ **5.** The piston pin bearing surface is shown at ___.

_____ **6.** The spring clip is shown at ___.

_____ **7.** The rod cap screw is shown at ___.

_____ **8.** The crankpin journal bearing surface is shown at ___.

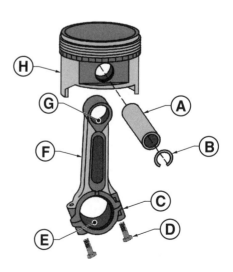

Crankshaft

_____ 1. The bearing journal is shown at ___.

_____ 2. The crankpin journal is shown at ___.

_____ 3. The crankgear is shown at ___.

_____ 4. The PTO is shown at ___.

_____ 5. The counterweights are shown at ___.

_____ 6. The throw is shown at ___.

_____ 7. The bearing journal is shown at ___.

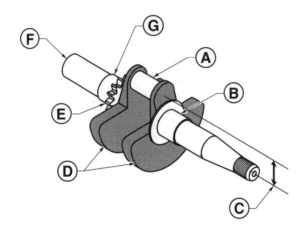

Name _____ Date _____

_____ **1.** The ___ is the engine component which consists of the cylinder bore, cooling fins on air-cooled engines, and valve train components, depending on the engine design.

_____ **2.** The ___ is a hole in an engine block that aligns and directs the piston during movement.

T   F   **3.** Approximately 70% of the energy released in an internal combustion engine is converted into work.

_____ **4.** ___ is the point at which the piston is closest to the cylinder head.
    A. TDC
    B. BDC
    C. MDC
    D. none of the above

_____ **5.** When bore and stroke are known, the displacement of a single-cylinder engine is found by applying the formula ___.
    A. $D = 0.7854 + B^2 + S$
    B. $D = 0.7854 \times \dfrac{B^2}{S}$
    C. $D = 0.7854 \times B^2 \times S$
    D. $D = 0.7854 \times \dfrac{S}{B^2}$

_____ **6.** A(n) ___ is an integral thin cast strip designed to provide efficient air circulation and dissipation of heat away from the engine cylinder block into the air stream.

_____ **7.** The crankcase ___ is an engine component that relieves crankcase pressure created by the reciprocating motion of the piston during engine operation.

_____ **8.** A(n) ___ is a cast aluminum alloy or cast iron engine component fastened to the end of the cylinder block farthest from the crankshaft.

_____ **9.** A(n) ___ is an engine component in which the cylinder block and cylinder head are cast as a single unit.

_____ **10.** A(n) ___ engine is an engine that has valves and related components located in the cylinder block.

T   F   **11.** Cast aluminum alloy cylinder blocks are lightweight and dissipate heat more rapidly than cast iron cylinder blocks.

T   F   **12.** Displacement is the volume that a piston displaces in an engine when it travels from TDC to BDC during the same piston stroke.

_____ **13.** The ___ is an engine component that converts the linear motion of the piston into rotary motion.

_____ **14.** A(n) ___ journal is a precision ground surface that provides a rotating pivot point to attach the connecting rod to the crankshaft.

_____ **15.** A(n) ___ is a protruding mass integrally cast into the crankshaft which partially balances the forces of a reciprocating piston and reduces the load on crankshaft bearing journals.

_____ **16.** The ___ is an extension of the crankshaft that allows an engine to transmit power to an application.
    A. flywheel
    B. bearing journal
    C. crankpin journal
    D. PTO

_____ **17.** Thermal ___ is the ability of a material to conduct and transfer heat.

_____ **18.** Ring ___ are the two parallel surfaces of the ring groove which function as the sealing surface for the piston ring.
    A. seals
    B. bands
    C. lands
    D. none of the above

T   F   **19.** A compression ring is the piston ring located in the ring groove farthest from the piston head.

T   F   **20.** A turbocharger raises the pressure and density of air entering the engine.

_____ **21.** A(n) ___ is a component used to reduce friction and to maintain clearance between stationary and rotating components of an engine.

T   F   **22.** An axial load is a load applied perpendicular to the shaft.

T   F   **23.** A nonferrous metal is any metal that contains iron.

_____ **24.** The ___ is a cast iron, aluminum, or zinc disk that is mounted at one end of the crankshaft to provide inertia for the engine.

_____ **25.** The crankshaft of a four-stroke cycle engine turns ___° to complete one operating cycle.
    A. 180
    B. 360
    C. 540
    D. 720

_____ **26.** ___ is the process of reducing or squeezing a charge from a large volume to a smaller volume in the combustion chamber.

_____ **27.** ___ is the rapid, oxidizing chemical reaction in which a fuel chemically combines with oxygen in the atmosphere and releases energy in the form of heat.

_____ **28.** The ___ event is an engine operation event in which spent gases are removed from the combustion chamber and released to the atmosphere.

T   F   **29.** Duration of valve overlap is between 10° – 20° of crankshaft rotation, depending on the engine design.

_____ **30.** The valve ___ is the machine stationary surface that mates with the valve face to seal the combustion chamber.

_____ **31.** A(n) ___ engine is a reciprocating internal combustion engine that ignites fuel by high compression.

_____ **32.** A(n) ___ is a protruding mass integrally cast into the crankshaft that partially balances the forces of a reciprocating piston and reduces the load on crankshaft bearing journals.

_____ **33.** The ___ is a device that applies a load to an operating engine and measures torque, load, speed, or horsepower.

_____ **34.** ___ efficiency is the ratio of volume available in the engine to the actual volume filled during operation.

_____ **35.** The ___ is a diesel engine component that functions as an ON/OFF valve to introduce fuel into the cylinder.

_____ **36.** A(n) ___ is an antifriction bearing component used to maintain the position and alignment of rolling elements.

T   F   **37.** Two-stroke cycle engines operate at higher speed and temperatures than four-stroke cycle engines.

T   F   **38.** A wiper ring is the piston ring located in the ring groove closest to the crankcase.

_____ **39.** ___ is the process of using the introduction of fresh air-fuel mixture to help remove exhaust gases from the cylinder in a two-stroke cycle engine.

_____ **40.** The ___ is an engine operation where the air-fuel mixture is introduced to fill the combustion chamber.

_____ **41.** A(n) ___ engine has valves and related components located within the cylinder heads and above the combustion chambers.

T   F   **42.** Turbochargers are installed on some liquid-cooled multiple-cylinder engines as one method of increasing engine output without changing engine dimensions or application size limitations.

T   F   **43.** Turbo boost is the time period between when the operator demands more power and the time when the intake air reaches maximum pressure for the desired power.

T   F   **44.** In the United States, the most common diesel fuel is Grade No. 4-D diesel fuel.

_____ **45.** A(n) ___ is a component that acts as a bypass or pressure-relief valve within a turbocharger.

T   F   **46.** An antifriction bearing consists of a fixed, nonmoving bearing surface that provides a low-friction support surface for rotating or sliding surfaces.

_____ **47.** A(n) ___ is a hollow shaft that connects the small end of the connecting rod to the piston.

_____ **48.** A(n) ___ is the boundary wall that separates the charge from the combustion by-products.

_____ **49.** ___ is a nonferrous metal alloy consisting of copper, lead, and tin or lead and tin.
      A. Babbitt
      B. Cladding
      C. Red brass
      D. Zinc

T   F   **50.** Two-stroke cycle engines do not require oil rings.

Bearings

_____ **1.** The bearings at ___ are roller bearings.

_____ **2.** The bearings at ___ are ball bearings.

_____ **3.** The bearings at ___ are integrally machined bearings.

_____ **4.** The bearings at ___ are sleeve bearings.

_____ **5.** The bearings at ___ are split-sleeve bearings.

_____ **6.** The bearings at ___ are DU® bearings.

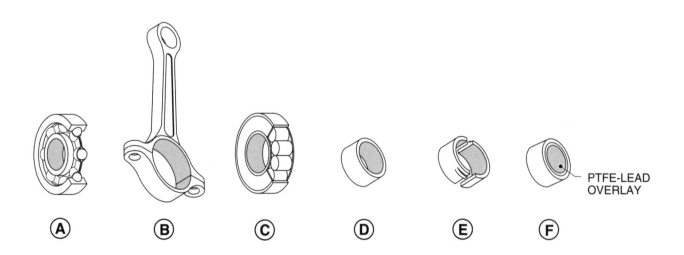

PTFE-LEAD
OVERLAY

Ⓐ   Ⓑ   Ⓒ   Ⓓ   Ⓔ   Ⓕ

Pistons

_____ **1.** The piston head at ___ has a flat shape.

_____ **2.** The piston head at ___ has an irregular, contoured shape.

_____ **3.** The piston head at ___ has a domed, contoured shape.

_____ **4.** The piston head at ___ has a dished, contoured shape.

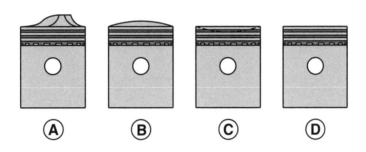

Ignition Event

_____ **1.** The flame front completes the burn.

_____ **2.** The spark occurs BTDC.

_____ **3.** The charge begins burning.

_____ **4.** The flame front spreads throughout the combustion chamber.

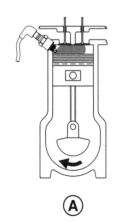 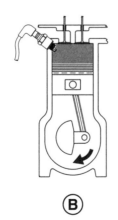 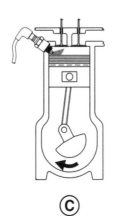 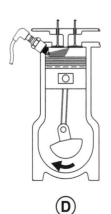

Name _____   Date _____

---

1. Oil leaking past the governor shaft bushing is more likely to be caused by a loss of crankcase vacuum than a worn bushing.

   True
   False

---

2. After an engine has completed one full operating cycle, how many degrees has the crankshaft rotated?

   A. 360°
   B. 720 °
   C. 1440°
   D. 180°

---

3. Upon examination of an engine that will not start after a complete overhaul, the technician finds that both the intake and exhaust valves are open at the same time when the piston is 1″ down the cylinder bore past TDC on the intake stroke.

   Technician A says that this phenomenon is valve overlap and it could not be the cause of the engine not starting.

   Technician B says that the cam gear timing is not indexed correctly with the crankgear.

   Which technician is correct?

   A. Technician A
   B. Technician B
   C. Both Technicians A and B
   D. Neither Technicians A nor B

---

4. In a typical Briggs & Stratton four-stroke cycle engine, how many times does the cam gear rotate with each revolution of the crankshaft?

   A. 1
   B. 2
   C. ½
   D. 4

---

5. The terms watt and horsepower are measurements of exactly the same value; that of the speed at which work is done.

   True
   False

---

6. A landscape contractor complains that his 16 HP 52″ commercial walk-behind rotary mower does not move through high grass fast enough. He asks that a higher horsepower engine be installed so he can mow the grass at a higher rate of speed.

Technician A says that installing a 20 HP Vanguard™ V-Twin engine would solve the problem.

Technician B says that this will not help the speed of the mower at all because torque cuts the grass, not horsepower. Which technician is correct?

    A. Technician A

    B. Technician B

    C. Both Technicians A and B

    D. Neither Technicians A nor B

7. When an engine has a compression ratio of 6:1, it means that the volume of the crankcase is one-sixth as much when the piston is closest to the crankshaft than it is when the piston is farthest from the crankshaft.

    True
    False

8. If an engine is operated on dry land at an ambient temperature of 60°F, the dynamometer indicates that it produces "x" number of watts. The same engine and dynamometer are then operated on dry land in an environment with an ambient temperature of 10°F. The engine watt output will:

    A. increase

    B. decrease

    C. stay exactly the same

    D. temperatures below 60°F have no effect on watt output

9. The throw of the crankshaft is equal to:

    A. ½ the stroke

    B. 2 times the stroke

    C. the length of the stroke

    D. none of the above

10. If the flywheel supplies the inertia an engine needs to operate properly, which of these statements is true?

    A. An engine equipped with a high-inertia flywheel shows an increase in horsepower compared to a duplicate engine equipped with a low-inertia flywheel.

    B. An engine equipped with a high-inertia flywheel will accelerate to top no-load speed a little slower than a duplicate engine equipped with a low-inertia flywheel.

    C. All Briggs & Stratton engines are designed with some component that supplies inertia.

    D. Both B and C

Name _____   Date _____

_____ **1.** The compression ratio of most small engines ranges between ___.
A. 5:1 and 9:1
B. 6:1 and 8.5:1
C. 5:1 and 8.5:1
D. 6:1 and 9:1

_____ **2.** During compression, heat is produced from the work applied by the ___.

_____ **3.** As the piston moves toward TDC, the volume of the combustion chamber is ___.

_____ **4.** ___ is the molecular attraction by which atoms and molecules are united throughout the mass.

_____ **5.** When gasoline is heated, it changes rapidly from a liquid to a(n) ___.

T   F   **6.** Gasoline molecules become less active as the temperature of the charge is raised.

T   F   **7.** Excessive compression can lead to detonation and preignition.

_____ **8.** Detonation is sometimes called ___.
A. knocking
B. spark knock
C. pinging
D. all of the above

_____ **9.** ___ is an undesirable engine condition which occurs when a small portion of a combustion chamber component or a particle in the combustion chamber becomes excessively heated and ignites the charge as it enters the combustion chamber.

T   F   **10.** Compression ratio is decreased when a large volume of combustion chamber deposits accumulate in the engine.

_____ **11.** ___ steel is a heat-resistive metal alloy consisting of cobalt, tungsten, and chromium.

_____ **12.** A greater than ___% difference between the compression readings on a two-cylinder engine indicates a loss of compression in the cylinder with lower pressure.

_____ **13.** ___ is the application of material to an engine component to improve wear resistance from load, heat, and chemical corrosion.

_____ **14.** When a gas is released from a pressurized container such as an aerosol spray can, the compressed gas ___.
A. releases heat
B. feels cool
C. all of the above
D. none of the above

35

_____ **15.** All Briggs & Stratton small engines use a ___° exhaust valve face angle.
A. 37½
B. 45
C. 60
D. none of the above

_____ **16.** A(n) ___ angle is the intentional deviation from a specification of two mating machine components to improve seating quality after a sufficient break-in period.

T   F **17.** Valve rotation is recommended on engines that use LP gas or propane.

T   F **18.** Aluminum is much harder than brass.

_____ **19.** ___ loading is the application of an undesirable unilateral force to an engine component or components.

_____ **20.** ___ conductivity is the ability of a material to conduct and transfer heat.

_____ **21.** A valve seat ___ is a separate machined engine component pressed into the cylinder block that provides the sealing surface for a valve.

T   F **22.** Some piston pins have the piston pin offset from center in the piston.

T   F **23.** An elliptical shape is an oval shape in which one-half is a mirror image of the other half.

T   F **24.** Unplated aluminum pistons are commonly used in aluminum cylinder bores.

_____ **25.** Piston ___ are a series of small holes machined into the oil ring groove surface of the piston.

_____ **26.** ___ growth is the increase in size of a material when heated, with little or no change back to original dimensions.

_____ **27.** ___ pressure is the internal spring force that expands a piston ring based on the design and properties of the material used.

_____ **28.** ___ is the process that causes the running surfaces of piston rings and the surface of the cylinder bore to conform to each other.

_____ **29.** Abrasive ___ is a cause of engine failure through the undesirable introduction of abrasive particles into a small engine.

T   F **30.** A slow break-in period for piston ring materials is 1 hr to 8 hr.

Adiabatic Process

_____ **1.** The piston at ___ is at BDC.

_____ **2.** The piston at ___ is moving toward TDC.

_____ **3.** The piston at ___ is at TDC.

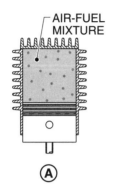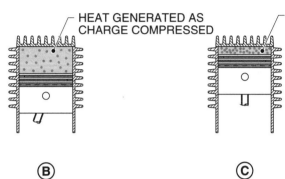

Valves

_____ **1.** The valve seats at ___ are integrally machined.

_____ **2.** The valve seats at ___ are valve-seat inserts.

_____ **3.** A two-piece-stem welded valve is shown at ___.

_____ **4.** A projection-tip welded valve is shown at ___.

_____ **5.** A one-piece valve is shown at ___.

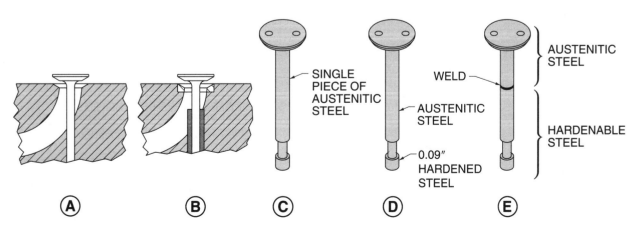

Piston Rings

_____ **1.** The piston ring twist at ___ is a positive twist.

_____ **2.** The piston ring twist at ___ is a negative twist.

_____ **3.** The piston ring at ___ is a compression ring.

_____ **4.** The piston ring at ___ is a wiper ring.

_____ **5.** The piston ring at ___ is an oil ring.

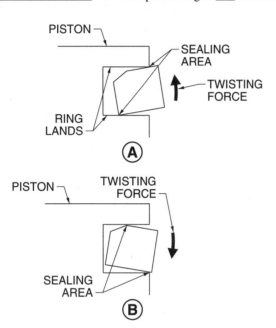

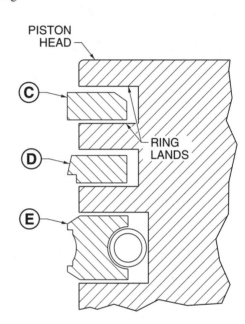

Interference Angle

_____ **1.** The valve face is shown at ___.

_____ **2.** The interference angle is shown at ___.

_____ **3.** The valve seat is shown at ___.

_____ **4.** The cylinder block is shown at ___.

_____ **5.** The valve interface at the point of contact is shown at ___.

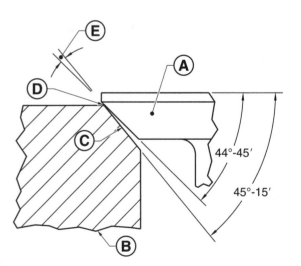

Name _____ Date _____

_____ **1.** With a compression ratio of 8:1, the charge is compressed into a space ___ the original volume of air-fuel mixture before the compression event.
A. 0.81
B. 0.18
C. ⅛
D. none of the above

_____ **2.** A(n) ___ process is a process in which heat is derived from the process itself.

_____ **3.** The charge enters the combustion chamber in a(n) ___ state.
A. solid
B. gaseous
C. all of the above
D. none of the above

_____ **4.** The energy required to compress the charge before combustion is typically ___% of the energy released during combustion.

T   F **5.** Inadequate compression is commonly caused by leaks.

T   F **6.** Piston ring assembly charts help to ensure the proper ring type and position.

T   F **7.** The energy required to initiate combustion is provided by the spark jumping across the gap in the electrode of the spark plug.

_____ **8.** ___ is an undesirable engine condition in which there is spontaneous combustion of a significant portion of the charge before the spark-induced flame front reaches it.

T   F **9.** The release of energy during detonation occurs at a much slower rate than by normal spark-induced ignition.

_____ **10.** Most exhaust valves used in Briggs & Stratton engines are made from ___ steel.

_____ **11.** ___ steel is a ferrous alloy primarily consisting of chromium or nickel.

_____ **12.** A(n) ___ surface is the portion of an engine component which interacts with a lubricated mating engine bearing surface during operation.

_____ **13.** Most hardfacing deposits on valves are approximately ___″ thick on the sealing surface or face of the valve.

_____ **14.** For optimum performance and durability, a ___° exhaust valve face angle is the industry standard.
A. 37½
B. 45
C. 60
D. none of the above

_____ **15.** All Briggs & Stratton small engines use a ___° intake valve angle.
    A. 30
    B. 45
    C. 30° or 45
    D. none of the above

_____ **16.** The valve ___ is the point of contact between the valve face and the valve seat.

T   F   **17.** The valve guide length to valve stem diameter ratio is typically 7:1.

T   F   **18.** Valve rotation provides improved temperature distribution in the valve head.

_____ **19.** ___ expansion is the expansion of a material when it is subjected to heat.

_____ **20.** A(n) ___ iron valve guide is a separate machined valve guide insert manufactured from a powdered iron compound that is heated and compressed to form the desired shape.

_____ **21.** Valve seats used in Briggs & Stratton engines are commonly hardfaced with ___.

T   F   **22.** Valve seat inserts are installed in the cylinder block using a press fit.

T   F   **23.** The offset piston pin design offers a quieter running engine by reducing piston wobble and related noise.

T   F   **24.** Free piston ring gap is the distance between the two ends of a piston ring in an uncompressed state.

_____ **25.** Ring ___ are the two parallel surfaces of the ring groove which function as the sealing surface for the piston ring.

_____ **26.** ___ pressure is the pressure applied from combustion gases to the piston ring, causing it to expand.

_____ **27.** A taper-faced compression ring is a piston ring that has approximately a(n) ___° taper angle on the running face.

_____ **28.** ___ is the process of using a hone with rigid Carborundum stones rotated in the cylinder bore to remove small surface irregularities and remove any glazing.

T   F   **29.** A fast break-in period for piston ring materials is 1 hr to 8 hr.

T   F   **30.** A convolution is an irregularly-shaped pocket on the surface of a cylinder that acts as a small reservoir for lubricating oil.

Detonation

_____ **1.** Spark-induced ignition occurs at ___.

_____ **2.** Combustion occurs at ___.

_____ **3.** Detonation occurs at ___.

_____ **4.** Knocking/pinging occur at ___.

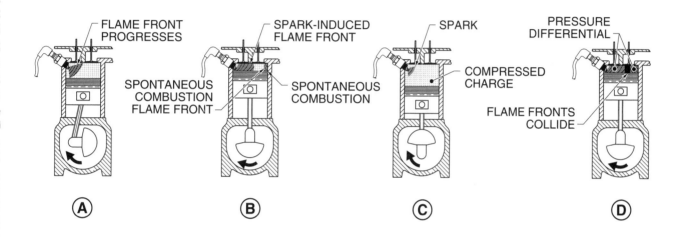

Preignition

_____ **1.** Preignition occurs at ___.

_____ **2.** Spark-induced ignition occurs at ___.

_____ **3.** The flame fronts converge at ___.

_____ **4.** Knocking/pinging occur at ___.

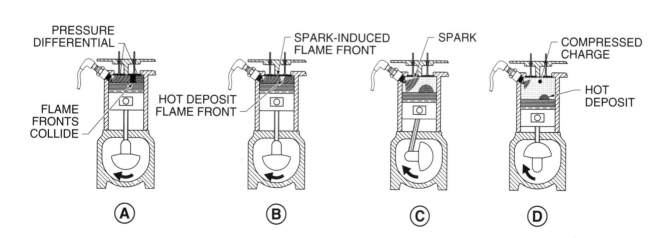

Thermal Expansion

Round to the accuracy of the coefficient.

_____ 1. The new length of the rod at A, when the temperature is increased 200°F is ___″.

_____ 2. The new length of the rod at B, when the temperature is increased 350°F is ___″.

_____ 3. The new length of the rod at C, when the temperature is increased 175°F is ___″.

_____ 4. The new length of the rod at D, when the temperature is increased 225°F is ___″.

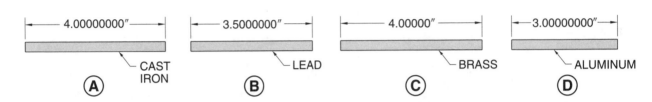

|←——— 4.00000000″ ———→| |←——— 3.5000000″ ———→| |←——— 4.00000″ ———→| |←——3.00000000″——→|

CAST IRON   LEAD   BRASS   ALUMINUM

(A)   (B)   (C)   (D)

COEFFICIENT OF THERMAL EXPANSION		
Metal	**Linear Expansion per Unit***	**Temperature °F†**
Aluminum	0.00001244	68
Brass	0.00001	76 – 212
Cast iron	0.00000655	68
Lead	0.0000163	212
Nickel	0.00000700	68
Steel (carbon)	0.00000633	68
Tin	0.00001496	64 – 212

* length per °F in inches
† temperature at which coeffiecient of thermal expansion was determined

Leaking Exhaust Valve

_____ 1. Maverick air enters the combustion chamber at ___.

_____ 2. Maverick air enters the cylinder head at ___.

_____ 3. The intake port is shown at ___.

_____ 4. The exhaust port is shown at ___.

_____ 5. An exhaust valve leak is shown at ___.

_____ 6. The piston is moving toward BDC at ___.

1. If an exhaust valve leaks during engine operation, maverick air is drawn into the combustion chamber, causing a lean air-fuel mixture. What symptoms will a leaking exhaust valve cause during engine operation?

    A. The engine may backfire through the exhaust system

    B. The engine may be difficult to start

    C. The engine may exhibit a loss of power

    D. all of the above

2. As the compression ratio is increased, the loads and stresses on internal engine parts become more severe.

    True
    False

3. Valve sticking can be caused by gum, varnish, or combustion deposit buildup on the valve stem and in the valve guide.

    True
    False

4. One quick and simple preliminary test for compression on a Briggs & Stratton engine is to quickly rotate the engine counterclockwise and observe the engine for a sharp rebound. Why must the engine be rotated counterclockwise as opposed to the normal direction of operation?

    A. The engine will not rebound at all if rotated clockwise.

    B. The compression release is only effective when rotating clockwise.

    C. It is easier to compress the exhaust charge than the intake charge.

    D. Counterclockwise rotation on the power stroke eliminates the compression release system as it is ineffective during this stroke.

5. If the compression of the charge and the resultant heat causes the fine droplets of gasoline to break apart, providing more vapor for the combustion process:

    A. The highest compression ratio possible should be incorporated in all gasoline engines.

    B. The higher the combustion chamber temperature, the more performance the engine provides.

    C. The leaner the engine should be run.

    D. none of the above

6. Offset pistons are used to compensate for offset crankpin journals.

    True
    False

7. A Cobalite™ hardfaced exhaust valve should always be resurfaced during valve service to ensure long valve life.

   True
   False

8. A common cause of insufficient valve rotation on a gasoline-powered air-cooled engine is:

   A. Lack of clearance between the valve stem and the valve guide
   B. Improperly positioned valve spring
   C. Excessive combustion deposits
   D. all of the above

9. Valve rotation is not encouraged in air-cooled engines that are powered by LP/propane gas. Which of the following statements is incorrect?

   A. The combustion chamber and combustion gas temperatures are higher in LP/propane gas applications.
   B. The wiping action of the rotating valve may result in a loss of material on the valve and/or valve seat.
   C. LP/propane gas contains much more lubricant, which can cause combustion deposits.
   D. The temperature of the exhaust valve in an LP/propane-powered application is commonly much higher than in a gasoline-powered application.

10. The amount of thermal expansion is dependent on several factors, including the quantity of material at various locations in a component. Which part of the piston expands the most during normal engine operation?

    A. The piston head
    B. The piston pin bore area
    C. The skirt
    D. The ring lands

11. A newly overhauled engine exhibits excessive white/blue smoke at idle top no-load speeds and while under load. Which of the following could be the cause?

    A. Improper valve stem clearance
    B. An incorrectly installed wiper ring
    C. Excessive crankshaft end play
    D. A missing head gasket

12. An engine is brought in for service with the customer complaint of lack of power, high oil consumption, and repeated blown head gaskets. Upon disassembly, all of the piston ring gaps are found to be aligned and the head gasket is partially burnt, but there are no signs of wear in the cylinder, rings, or any other compression component except a slightly burnt exhaust valve and worn valve guide.

    Which of the following is least likely to be the cause of the symptoms the customer described?

    A. The burnt exhaust valve
    B. The ring alignment
    C. The burnt head gasket
    D. The valve guide

Name _____ Date _____

T   F   **1.** The most common fuel used in small engines is gasoline.

_____   **2.** A(n) ___ fuel is a fuel derived from previously living things that have been preserved in a mineralized or petrified state.

_____   **3.** A gasoline molecule contains ___ atoms of carbon and ___ atoms of hydrogen.
　　　　　　A. 4; 14
　　　　　　B. 6; 16
　　　　　　C. 8; 18
　　　　　　D. 10; 20

_____   **4.** ___ ratio is the specific air-fuel ratio (by weight) of atmospheric air to fuel at which the most efficient and complete combustion occurs.

_____   **5.** ___ is a toxic gas produced by incomplete combustion of gasoline or other HC-based fuels.

_____   **6.** ___ is the spontaneous combustion of the charge commonly caused by low octane fuel or excessive compression ratio.

_____   **7.** The ___ is the octane number that affects engine knock at low to medium speed.

_____   **8.** A minimum AKI of ___ is recommended for all Briggs & Stratton overhead valve (OHV) engines.

T   F   **9.** Vaporization is the process in which a liquid is sufficiently cooled to change states of matter from a liquid to a vapor.

T   F   **10.** LPG requires higher ignition temperatures and burns slower than gasoline.

_____   **11.** ___ is an alcohol additive that is distilled from methane gas and used for gasoline.

_____   **12.** A(n) ___ is an engine component that provides the required air-fuel mixture to the combustion chamber based on engine operating speed and load.

_____   **13.** A(n) ___ is a narrowed portion of a tube.

_____   **14.** A bowl ___ is a passage drilled into the carburetor connecting the fuel bowl to the atmosphere.
　　　　　　A. tube
　　　　　　B. rod
　　　　　　C. vent
　　　　　　D. none of the above

_____   **15.** A ___ plate is a flat plate placed in the carburetor body between the throttle plate and air intake that restricts air flow to help start a cold engine.
　　　　　　A. choke
　　　　　　B. throttle
　　　　　　C. choke or throttle
　　　　　　D. none of the above

_____ **16.** A(n) ___ system is a rubber bulb that is depressed to force a metered amount of fuel into the venturi to help start a cold engine.

_____ **17.** Under maximum load, the throttle plate is at ___ and the engine is producing maximum torque.

T   F **18.** A needle and seat provide a tapered seal to regulate the flow of fuel into the carburetor.

T   F **19.** An updraft carburetor is a carburetor that has the air intake opening above the fuel bowl.

T   F **20.** A check ball is a component that functions as a one-way valve to allow fuel to flow in one direction only.

_____ **21.** A(n) ___ is a rubber membrane that separates chambers and flexes when a pressure differential occurs.

_____ **22.** A(n) ___ is a unit of area measurement equal to one thousandth of a millimeter (0.001 mm).

_____ **23.** A fuel ___ is an engine component that pressurizes the fuel system to advance fuel from the fuel tank to the carburetor.

T   F **24.** A check valve is a valve that allows the flow of material in one direction.

T   F **25.** Air density is the mass of air per unit volume.

_____ **26.** ___ is a product of incomplete combustion and is formed when an HC molecule is broken during combustion with a deficiency of available O_2.
    A. Carbon dioxide
    B. Carbon monoxide
    C. Nitric oxide
    D. Oxides of nitrogen

T   F **27.** Most catalytic converters used with small engines are monolithic converters designed specifically to reduce hydrocarbon and CO exhaust emissions.

_____ **28.** The three main undesirable compounds generated in exhaust gases from small engines are hydrocarbons, carbon monoxide, and ___.
    A. carbon dioxide
    B. nitrogen dioxide
    C. nitric oxide
    D. nitrogen oxide

_____ **29.** ___ is a chemical process that supports and accelerates a desired chemical reaction without chemically changing the catalyst component.

_____ **30.** A(n) ___ is a device that contains a catalyst used to reduce the toxicity of emissions from an internal combustion engine.

T   F **31.** The air-fuel ratio of an LPG-fueled engine is affected by altitude changes.

T   F **32.** Liquid gasoline is not flammable.

_____ **33.** Dinitrogen monoxide is also known as ___ gas.

_____ **34.** ___ is a heavy, colorless gas that does not support combustion.
    A. Carbon dioxide
    B. Nitrogen dioxide
    C. Nitric oxide
    D. Nitrogen oxide

_____ **35.** Because of the vast number of geometrically aligned holes, a catalytic element is commonly referred to as a(n) ___.

Carburetor Operation

_____ **1.** Higher pressure outside the engine is shown at ___.

_____ **2.** The air-fuel mixture is shown at ___.

_____ **3.** Air is shown at ___.

_____ **4.** Fuel vapor is shown at ___.

_____ **5.** Lower pressure in the combustion chamber is shown at ___.

_____ **6.** Liquid fuel is shown at ___.

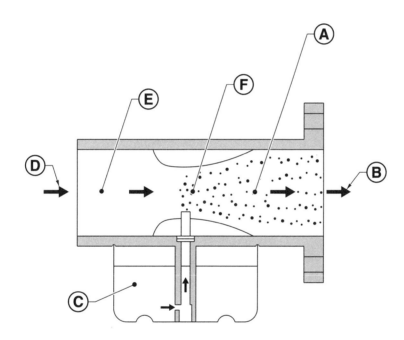

TEST 2
FUEL SYSTEM

CHAPTER 5

Name _____   Date _____

T   F   **1.** A hydrocarbon molecule is a molecule held together by a tight bond between hydrogen and carbon atoms that occurs naturally in all fossil fuels.

_____ **2.** ___ is the rapid, oxidizing chemical reaction in which a fuel chemically combines with oxygen in the atmosphere and releases energy in the form of heat.

_____ **3.** The most efficient and complete combustion of gasoline occurs when there are ___ parts atmospheric air for every 1 part fuel.
       A. 9.0
       B. 14.3
       C. 14.7
       D. 15.4

_____ **4.** The ___ excess air factor is a numerical value assigned to represent the stoichiometric ratio of atmospheric air to any hydrocarbon fuel.

_____ **5.** ___ is the ability of a fuel sample to resist engine knock and/or ping.

_____ **6.** The ___ is the numerical value assigned to gasoline that indicates the ability to eliminate knocking and/or pinging in an operating engine.

_____ **7.** The ___ is the octane number that affects engine knock at high speed and performance in severe operating conditions and under load.

T   F   **8.** Volatility is the propensity of a liquid to become a vapor.

_____ **9.** ___ is the stoppage of fuel flow caused by internal pressure of a fuel vapor bubble that equals or exceeds the ambient fuel pressure.

T   F   **10.** Alcohol is a fuel, or fuel additive, used to enhance the octane rating of gasoline.

_____ **11.** Atmospheric pressure at sea level is ___ psi.

_____ **12.** ___ principle states that air flowing through a narrowed portion of a tube increases in velocity and decreases in pressure.

_____ **13.** The ___ is the main passage in the carburetor which directs air from the atmosphere and air-fuel mixture to the combustion chamber.

_____ **14.** A ___ plate is a round movable disk that pivots on a shaft, regulating air and fuel flow inside a carburetor.
       A. choke
       B. throttle
       C. choke or throttle
       D. none of the above

49

T   F   **15.** True idle is the carburetor setting when the throttle plate linkage is resting against the idle speed adjusting screw after idle air-fuel mixture adjustment.

_____   **16.** A(n) ___ is a passage in the carburetor that directs air and atmospheric pressure into the main and idle circuits to facilitate the mixture of air and fuel.

_____   **17.** A(n) ___ jet is a carburetor component that contains a fixed orifice jet that meters and controls fuel flow to the idle circuit of the carburetor.

T   F   **18.** Engine horsepower decreases by 5.5% for each 1000′ above sea level.

T   F   **19.** A downdraft carburetor is a carburetor that has the air intake opening below the fuel bowl.

T   F   **20.** The fuel cup is a reservoir located high inside the fuel tank.

_____   **21.** A fuel ___ is a fuel system component that removes foreign particles by straining fuel from the fuel tank.

_____   **22.** ___ pressure is the force derived from the mass of a contained liquid such as fuel stored in a fuel tank.

T   F   **23.** Filter mesh screens are rated at the number of openings per sq in.

T   F   **24.** A float is a carburetor component that floats at a specific level to regulate the opening and closing of the needle and seat.

T   F   **25.** A sidedraft carburetor is a carburetor that has an air intake opening below the fuel bowl and parallel to a horizontal plane.

T   F   **26.** HC emissions are caused by unburned, partially burned, or raw fuel.

_____   **27.** A ___ is a stamped metal housing that reduces exhaust noise and secures the catalytic element directly in line with the exhaust stream.
   A. catalyst
   B. catalytic converter
   C. muffler shell
   D. reducer

_____   **28.** A(n) ___ test is used to determine the composition and volatility characteristics of a given fuel sample.

_____   **29.** The octane requirement for an engine is primarily based on the ___.

T   F   **30.** In the 1970s, ethyl alcohol was used as an alternative fuel and renewable energy source.

T   F   **31.** Nitric oxide is more toxic than other oxides of nitrogen.

_____   **32.** A(n) ___ is a specialized exhaust system device that utilizes a single catalytic element to convert hydrocarbons and CO.

_____   **33.** ___ temperature is the temperature of the surrounding environment.

_____   **34.** ___ is a gaseous fuel that consists of propane, propylene, butane, and butylene in various mixtures.

_____   **35.** A(n) ___ test is used to determine the amount of pressure produced from the vaporization process.

Carburetor Design

_____ **1.** The carburetor shown at A is a(n) ___ carburetor.

_____ **2.** The carburetor shown at B is a(n) ___ carburetor.

_____ **3.** The carburetor shown at C is a(n) ___ carburetor.

_____ **4.** The carburetor shown at D is a(n) ___ carburetor.

Name   Date

1. A Briggs & Stratton engine equipped with a Vacu-Jet carburetor should be adjusted with the fuel tank full.

    True
    False

2. The automatic choke system found on vertical crankshaft Vacu-Jet and Pulsa-Jet carburetors operates using manifold vacuum. The choke spring attached to the diaphragm:

    A. Opens the choke after the engine has built up sufficient manifold vacuum
    B. Closes the choke in the absence of manifold vacuum
    C. Partially closes the choke plate when the engine is under heavy load
    D. Both B and C

3. A completely-blocked high speed air bleed can commonly cause an engine to run very rich under load.

    True
    False

4. The throttle plate in a Briggs & Stratton carburetor:

    A. Opens and closes the emulsion tube
    B. Decreases the venturi size
    C. Increases the venturi size
    D. Increases or decreases the difference in air pressure within the venturi

5. The stoichiometric ratio for common pump gasoline is 14.7:1.

    True
    False

6. Gasoline blended for use in the winter is highly volatile compared to gasoline blended for use in the summer.

    True
    False

7. The octane rating of a fuel is a good indicator of how much power the fuel can deliver during oxidation.

    True
    False

53

8. An engine exhibits hunting and surging while operating at idle and top no-load speeds. The hunting and surging is not evident when the engine is operated under moderate to heavy loads. Which of the following is the most probable cause of these symptoms?

    A. A blocked idle circuit air bleed

    B. An incorrect float setting

    C. A partially blocked fixed orifice main jet

    D. none of the above

9. An engine equipped with an internally vented carburetor will exhibit ___ from the exhaust system if the air cleaner becomes more than 70% clogged.

    A. Black smoke

    B. White smoke

    C. No smoke

    D. Blue/gray smoke

10. A new engine on a clear water pump operated at an elevation of 6000′ will experience some degree of performance problems. Which of the following is most accurate as to the nature of the anticipated performance problem?

    A. Reduced horsepower output/engine running richer than normal at all speeds and loads.

    B. Reduced horsepower output/engine running leaner than normal at all speeds and loads.

    C. The engine will be hard to start cold/run lean under load.

    D. The engine will idle poorly but maintain horsepower under load.

11. A dry bulb and a wet bulb primer system work in conjunction with the choke plate to provide easy cold starting of the engine.

    True
    False

12. A horizontal shaft engine featuring a carburetor with a pilot jet exhibits the following symptoms:

    Hard to start cold

    Hunts and surges under load (only)

    Runs well at idle and top no-load speeds

Technician A says that the cause of the symptoms is a partially blocked fixed main jet orifice.

Technician B says that the pilot jet fixed jet orifice is partially blocked.

Which technician is most likely to be correct?

    A. Technician A

    B. Technician B

    C. Both Technicians A and B

    D. Neither Technicians A nor B

Name _____ Date _____

_____ **1.** A(n) ___ system is a system that maintains a desired engine speed regardless of the load applied to the engine.

_____ **2.** Top ___ speed is the top speed setting an engine achieves without any parasitic load from equipment components.

_____ **3.** A(n) ___ device is a governor system component attached through linkage to the throttle plate of the carburetor to sense changes in engine speed.

T   F   **4.** The governed speed of an engine is the speed obtained at the balance point between the forces of the speed-sensing device and the governor spring.

T   F   **5.** Under load, most engines experience an increase in speed whether they have a fixed or a movable throttle plate.

_____ **6.** A(n) ___ governor system is a system which uses force from moving air produced by rotating flywheel fins to sense engine speed.
   A. flywheel
   B. pneumatic
   C. rotating
   D. force

_____ **7.** Based on the ___, governed speed may or may not be the top no-load speed or the governed speed of the engine.
   A. size of the engine
   B. diameter of the pistons
   C. throttle control position
   D. none of the above

T   F   **8.** With the engine OFF, the throttle control can be set to stretch the governor spring to hold the throttle plate in WOT position.

T   F   **9.** A change in governor blade material, mass, or angle of air deflection affects overall governor performance on the engine.

_____ **10.** ___ length is the overall dimension of the spring when unloaded.

_____ **11.** Pneumatic force from rotating flywheel fins on a governor blade varies depending on ___.
   A. engine speed
   B. governor blade position
   C. governor blade configuration
   D. all of the above

T   F   **12.** High throttle plate torque tends to open the throttle plate.

55

_____ 13. When the throttle plate is moved toward WOT position, torque is ___.
    A. increased
    B. reduced
    C. not affected
    D. none of the above

_____ 14. A(n) ___ governor system is a governor system that uses a gear assembly that meshes with the camshaft or other engine components to sense and maintain the desired engine speed.

_____ 15. A(n) ___ governor system is a governor system that uses a limited angle torque motor in place of the governor spring and speed-sensing device used in a mechanical governor system.

_____ 16. A(n) ___ is a rotating part of an electronic motor consisting of a segmented iron core or permanent magnet mounted on the motor shaft.

_____ 17. A governor ___ spring is an electronic governor system component that applies force to close the throttle plate.

_____ 18. Governor ___ is the amount of rpm decrease between the top no-load governed speed and the rpm where power is delivered.

_____ 19. Governor systems limit the amount of horsepower available by controlling engine ___.

_____ 20. ___ is the undesirable slow changing of engine rpm in a cyclical pattern when set at a desired speed.
    A. Hunting
    B. Humming
    C. Surging
    D. none of the above

_____ 21. Governed ___ is a governed system function that allows an engine to accept light to moderate loads at idle speed without stalling the engine.

Throttle Plate Position

_____ 1. The throttle plate at ___ is shown in the WOT position.

_____ 2. The throttle plate at ___ is shown with the engine at top no-load speed.

_____ 3. The throttle plate at ___ is shown with the engine at governed speed.

SPEED-SENSING
DEVICE FORCE
BALANCED
AGAINST
GOVERNOR
SPRING FORCE

THROTTLE
PLATE
OPENED
OR CLOSED
BASED ON
ENGINE RPM

A

GOVERNOR SPRING
PULLS THROTTLE PLATE
TOWARD WOT POSITION

SPEED-SENSING
DEVICE FORCE
OVERCOMES GOVERNOR
SPRING FORCE

FLYWHEEL
FINS PRODUCE
PNEUMATIC
FORCE

THROTTLE
PLATE
CLOSES

B

GOVERNOR
SPRING

SPEED-
SENSING
DEVICE

LINKAGE

ENGINE
FLYWHEEL

FIN

ENGINE NOT OPERATING

C

Name _____ Date _____

_____ 1. A(n) ___ load is a resistive force opposing engine forces.

_____ 2. A(n) ___ load is any load applied to an engine that is over and above the frictional load of an engine.

_____ 3. A(n) ___ spring is a governor system component that pulls the throttle plate toward the wide open throttle position.

T   F   4. The speed-sensing device monitors any increase or decrease in engine speed.

T   F   5. Early internal combustion engine governor systems used only the applied load for speed and torque control.

_____ 6. A(n) ___ blade is a movable metal or plastic blade which deflects air from flywheel fins to act as the speed-sensing device of a pneumatic governor system.
    A. air
    B. governor
    C. flywheel
    D. none of the above

T   F   7. The governor spring is the only force on the throttle plate when the engine is OFF.

T   F   8. Spring rates are expressed as lb/degree rates.

_____ 9. Spring ___ is the force necessary to stretch the spring one unit of length.

_____ 10. Governor blades may be mounted in the ___ position.
    A. vertical
    B. horizontal
    C. vertical or horizontal
    D. none of the above

T   F   11. Low throttle plate torque tends to open the throttle plate.

T   F   12. Most throttle shafts are slightly offset in the bore of the carburetor by .001″ – 018″.

_____ 13. A force differential is the measured difference in forces acting on ___.
    A. a single object
    B. two objects
    C. all of the above
    D. none of the above

T   F   14. When a curved governor blade is at top no-load speed position, it provides the governed speed and stability of a flat governor blade.

_____ 15. A(n) ___ motor is a DC motor used to control governor system components in an electronic governor system.

_____ 16. A(n) ___ field coil is a coil of wire attached to a segmented iron core that produces a magnetic field when current is passed through it.

_____ **17.** A(n) ___ effect is an effect based on the theory that less time is required to accelerate mass that is already in motion.

_____ **18.** A governor ___ curve is a combination of rpm decrease and maximum brake horsepower curves.

_____ **19.** ___ is the undesirable quick changing of engine rpm when set at a desired speed.
  A. Hunting
  B. Searching
  C. Selecting
  D. none of the above

_____ **20.** The ___ limit is the last point at which a material can be deformed and still return to its original physical dimensions.

_____ **21.** ___ is the undesirable motion of governor system components caused by engine vibration and governor system friction characteristics.

LAT Motor

_____ **1.** The linkage to the throttle plate is shown at ___.

_____ **2.** The governor springs return is shown at ___.

_____ **3.** The inductive field coil is shown at ___.

_____ **4.** The segmented iron core is shown at ___.

_____ **5.** The armature is shown at ___.

Fixed Throttle Plate Carburetor

_____ **1.** The needle and seat are shown at ___.

_____ **2.** The choke plate is shown at ___.

_____ **3.** The float is shown at ___.

_____ **4.** The throttle plate is shown at ___.

1. A small arc welder using an engine equipped with a mechanical governor system is brought in for repair. The customer complaint is that although the engine reaches the correct top no-load speed, when the user begins to weld, the engine rpm decreases to the point that the welder can no longer produce the proper amperage to perform the welding task at hand. The quality of the weld is very questionable as the output of the welder is not dependable. Other than the abrupt decrease in engine rpm under load, the engine operates without any problems.

    Technician A says that to correct this problem, install a higher rated governor spring and increase the top no-load speed of the engine so the rpm decrease under load is reduced.

    Technician B says that to correct this problem, install a lighter rated spring and perform the normal fixed speed governor adjustment procedures.

    Which technician is correct?

    A. Technician A

    B. Technician B

    C. Both Technicians A and B

    D. Each technician is partially correct

2. The primary purpose of the governor system on a Briggs & Stratton engine is to prevent overspeeding, which can cause engine damage.

    True
    False

3. After servicing the carburetor, a technician is performing a complete governor system adjustment. The governor system on the engine has two springs: the governed idle spring and the normal primary governor spring. Which of the two speed settings is adjusted first?

    A. The top no-load speed

    B. The governed idle speed

    C. Either can be adjusted first

    D. All engine speeds are preset

4. Some Briggs & Stratton engines are equipped with a feature known as governed idle. This governor system feature allows the engine to accept light loads at idle without stalling the engine.

    True
    False

5. When performing and completing a static governor adjustment, what is the relative position of the flyweights attached to the governor gear compared to the governor gear shaft? What is the relative position of the governor cup compared to the governor gear shaft?

    A. The flyweights are fully retracted toward the governor gear shaft and the cup is in the fully extended position away from the base of the governor gear shaft.

    B. The flyweights are fully extended outward away from the governor gear shaft and the cup is fully retracted toward the base of the governor gear shaft.

    C. The flyweights are fully retracted toward the governor gear shaft and the cup is fully retracted toward the base of the governor gear shaft.

    D. Both the flyweights and governor cup are fully extended away from the governor gear shaft.

6. Some Briggs & Stratton engines are equipped with a governor lever arm that has various speedsetting holes. If an engine hunts and surges at top no-load speed, the governor spring could be moved farther away from the pivot of the governor lever arm to attempt to reduce the hunting and surging.

    True
    False

7. All engines with a pneumatic or mechanical govenor system experience some degree of rpm decrease when placed under moderate to heavy loads.

Technician A says that the reason for this is that the engine has a short but finite time to intake, combust, and evacuate the combustion chamber to produce torque. When the engine is under load, the speed decrease occurs to allow more time to intake more fuel cornbust it and evacuate the combustion chamber, producing more torque.

Technician B says that the engine speed decreases due to the mechanical imperfections found in any governor system. The time lag before the spring(s) or throttle plate can respond is responsible for the rpm decrease.

Which technician is correct?

    A. Technician A

    B. Technician B

    C. Both Technicians A and B

    D. Neither Technicians A nor B

8. When the ignition switch on a lawn tractor is turned to the off position while the engine is running at top no-load speed, the spark to the combustion chamber is interrupted and the engine coasts down to a stop. Which of the following statements best describes the response of the governor system during the coast-down period?

    A. The governor system slowly closes the throttle plate in the carburetor.

    B. The governor system remains motionless.

    C. The governor spring immediately pulls the throttle plate to the idle position.

    D. The governor system opens the throttle plate progressively wider as the engine speed decreases, resulting in a WOT position when the engine stops.

Name _____   Date _____

_____ **1.** ___ is energy created by the flow of electrons in a conductor.

_____ **2.** Electrons are the parts of the atom that have a ___ electrical charge.
    A. positive
    B. negative
    C. positive or negative
    D. none of the above

T   F   **3.** Neutrons have a positive electrical charge.

T   F   **4.** Most small engine electrical systems are not capable of inflicting a severe electrical shock.

T   F   **5.** In a magnet, similar poles attract.

_____ **6.** A(n) ___ electron is an electron that is capable of jumping in or out of the outer orbit.

_____ **7.** A(n) ___ is a complete path that controls the rate and direction of electron flow on which voltage is applied.

_____ **8.** A(n) ___ is a device that uses electricity, such as the starter motor, lights, or other application accessories.

T   F   **9.** Voltage causes electrons to move in a circuit.

T   F   **10.** It is possible to have electron flow without voltage.

_____ **11.** The voltage source for most small engine applications is a(n) ___ V battery.

_____ **12.** ___ is the state of an object as negative or positive.

_____ **13.** Resistance is ___.
    A. opposition to electron flow
    B. measured in ohms
    C. both A and B
    D. none of the above

_____ **14.** A(n) ___ is an undesirable complete circuit path that bypasses the intended path and has very little resistance.

_____ **15.** A(n) ___ is half of a cycle.

_____ **16.** ___ is the international unit of frequency equal to one cycle per second.
    A. Milliamp
    B. Micron
    C. Hertz
    D. none of the above

_____ **17.** A(n) ___ is an electrical component that converts AC to DC by allowing the current to flow in only one direction.

_____ **18.** A(n) ___ circuit is a circuit that has two or more components connected so that there is only one path for current flow.

_____ **19.** A(n) ___ switch is a switch that is operated by a person.

_____ **20.** A(n) ___ switch is a switch that stops the flow of current any time current limits are reached.

_____ **21.** A(n) ___ switch is a switch that is operated by the movement of an object.

_____ **22.** A(n) ___ is an overcurrent protection device with a thin metal strip that melts and opens the circuit when a short circuit or overcurrent condition occurs.

_____ **23.** ___ law is a law that states the relationship between voltage, current, and resistance in any circuit.

_____ **24.** ___ is an atomic level force derived from the atomic structure and motion of certain orbiting electrons in a substance.

_____ **25.** A(n) ___ is a charging system device that produces AC voltage and amperage.

T   F   **26.** A coil is a circular wound wire consisting of noninsulated conductors arranged to produce lines of magnetic flux.

T   F   **27.** For maximum induced electron flow, the lines of magnetic flux must be 90° to the conductor.

_____ **28.** A(n) ___ is an electrical component that has a continuous copper wire wound on separate stubs exposing the wire to a magnetic field.

_____ **29.** A(n) ___ is an electrical component that stores voltage.

_____ **30.** A(n) ___ is an instrument used to measure the specific gravity of a liquid.

_____ **31.** Cold cranking amps is the number of amps produced by a battery for ___ while maintaining 1.2 V per cell.
  A. 30 sec at 0°F
  B. 30 sec at 32°F
  C. 60 sec at 0°F
  D. 60 sec at 32°F

_____ **32.** The ___ system is a system that provides a high-voltage spark in the combustion chamber at the proper time.

_____ **33.** The ___ winding is a coil in which high voltage is induced for use at the spark plug.

_____ **34.** A(n) ___ is a capacitor used in an ignition system that stores voltage and resists any change in voltage.

_____ **35.** A(n) ___ is a semiconductor that is normally an open circuit until voltage is applied, which switches it to the conducting state in one direction.
  A. VMS
  B. DMM
  C. SCR
  D. none of the above

_____ **36.** A(n) ___ starting system is a group of electrical components activated by the operator to rotate the crankshaft when starting an engine.

_____ **37.** The ___ gear is a gear on the starter motor that follows the helix to engage and drive the flywheel ring gear.

_____ **38.** A starter ___ is an electrical switch with internal contacts opened or closed using a magnetic field produced by a coil.

_____ **39.** ___ are carbon components in contact with the commutator that carry battery current to operate the starter motor.

T   F   **40.** Most outdoor power equipment requires a solenoid to allow a low amperage switch to activate the high amperage starter motor circuit.

_____ **41.** A(n) ___ is an electrical control device used to allow, interrupt, or direct the flow of electricity through a circuit.

T   F   **42.** Mechanical switches are classified as normally open or normally closed.

_____ **43.** A(n) ___ switch incorporates an actuator mechanism that has three distinct positions that can allow, interrupt, or redirect current flow according to design requirements.

_____ **44.** ___ logic is a system of symbolic logic that results in one of two possible answers.

_____ **45.** The actuator mechanism in a double-throw switch is typically a lever located in the ___ part of the switch body.
　　　　　A. right
　　　　　B. left
　　　　　C. center
　　　　　D. rear

T   F   **46.** Most OPE ignition switches have three or four spades.

_____ **47.** Test result truth tables that do not match OEM ___ are an indication of a malfunctioning switch.

T   F   **48.** A normally open switch allows current flow in the normal condition.

T   F   **49.** A headlight switch is typically a single-pole switch.

_____ **50.** A(n) ___ test is the measurement of a small resistance threshold between two points.
　　　　　A. continuity
　　　　　B. digital multimeter (DMM)
　　　　　C. insulation spot
　　　　　D. switch

Circuits

_____ **1.** A(n) ___ circuit is shown at A.

_____ **2.** A(n) ___ circuit is shown at B.

_____ **3.** A(n) ___ circuit is shown at C.

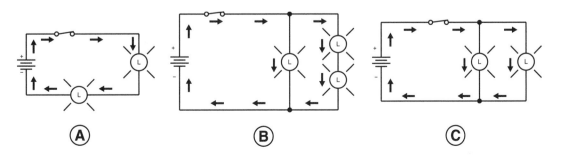

Breaker Point Ignition System

_____ **1.** The spark plug wire from the ___ winding is shown at A.

_____ **2.** The ignition ___ is shown at B.

_____ **3.** Primary and secondary ___ are shown at C.

_____ **4.** The ___ insert is shown at D.

_____ **5.** The ___ on the crankshaft is shown at E.

_____ **6.** The ___ is shown at F.

_____ **7.** The ___ is shown at G.

_____ **8.** The ___ is shown at H.

_____ **9.** The ___ is shown at I.

_____ **10.** The ___ is shown at J.

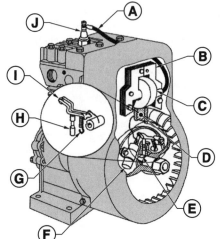

Breaker Points

_____ **1.** The ___ is shown at A.

_____ **2.** The ___ is shown at B.

_____ **3.** The ignition ___ is shown at C.

_____ **4.** The lamination ___ is shown at D.

_____ **5.** The flywheel ___ is shown at E.

_____ **6.** The ___ is shown at F.

_____ **7.** The ___ is shown at G.

_____ **8.** The ___ are shown at H.

_____ **9.** The ___ winding is shown at I.

_____ **10.** The ___ winding is shown at J.

T   F   **11.** The breaker points are shown closed.

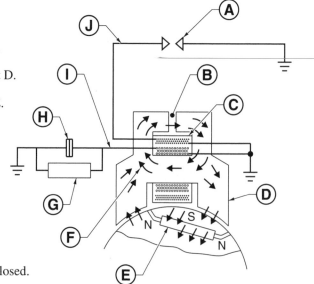

Name _____ Date _____

_____ 1. A(n) ___ is a material that allows the free flow of electrons.

_____ 2. Protons are the parts of the atom that have a ___ electrical charge.
    A. positive
    B. negative
    C. positive or negative
    D. none of the above

T   F 3. The nucleus is the center of the atom, which consists of protons and neutrons.

T   F 4. In a magnet, opposite poles attract.

T   F 5. The distance from the electron to the nucleus of the atom varies according to the number of electrons in the atom.

_____ 6. ___ is the amount of electrical pressure in a circuit.

_____ 7. A(n) ___ is a conductor which connects different parts of the circuit.

_____ 8. A(n) ___ is the unit of measure for electrical pressure difference between two points in a conductor or device.

T   F 9. A battery may be a source of voltage.

T   F 10. Voltage does not flow through a circuit.

_____ 11. ___ is the flow of electrons moving past a point in a circuit.

_____ 12. Current is measured in ___.

_____ 13. The smaller the AWG number, the ___.
    A. smaller the wire diameter
    B. larger the wire diameter
    C. shorter the wire length
    D. longer the wire length

_____ 14. A(n) ___ is one complete wave of alternating voltage that contains 360°.

_____ 15. ___ is the number of complete electrical cycles per second (cps).

_____ 16. A ___ is an electrical device that produces an AC sine wave as a wire coil is rotated in a magnetic field or as magnets are rotated inside a wire coil.
    A. rectifier
    B. generator
    C. battery
    D. none of the above

_____ 17. The United States uses AC voltage having a frequency of ___ Hz.

_____ 18. A(n) ___ is any component that is designed to start, stop, or redirect the flow of current in an electrical circuit.

_____ **19.** A(n) ___ circuit is a circuit that contains a combination of components connected in series and parallel.

_____ **20.** A(n) ___ circuit is a circuit that has two or more paths for current flow.

_____ **21.** A(n) ___ condition is a condition that occurs when the amount of current flowing in a circuit exceeds the design limit of the circuit.

_____ **22.** The prefix for micro is represented by ___.
        A. a lowercase letter m
        B. an uppercase letter M
        C. the Greek letter μ
        D. none of the above

_____ **23.** Electrical ___ are graphic illustrations used in electrical system diagrams to show the function of a device or component.

_____ **24.** Magnetic ___ is the invisible lines of force in a magnetic field.

T   F **25.** Induction is the production of voltage and current by the proximity and motion of a magnetic field or electric charge.

T   F **26.** A solenoid is a device that converts electrical energy into linear motion.

T   F **27.** An eddy current is desirable current induced in the metal structure of an electrical device due to the rate of change in the induced magnetic field.

_____ **28.** A(n) ___ is an electrical semiconductor device that can be used to convert AC to DC.

_____ **29.** A(n) ___ is an electrical energy storage device.

_____ **30.** ___ gravity is a comparison of the mass of a given sample volume compared to an equal volume of water.

_____ **31.** The ___ winding is a coil that induces voltage in the secondary winding.

_____ **32.** The spark ___ is the distance from the center electrode to the ground electrode on the spark plug.

_____ **33.** ___ is a magnetic field that is created around a conductor whenever current moves through the conductor.

_____ **34.** The ___ ignition system is an ignition system that uses electronic components in place of breaker points and a condenser.

_____ **35.** A(n) ___ starting system is a mechanical starter that commonly consists of a rope, pulley, and return spring used to manually rotate the crankshaft to start an engine.

_____ **36.** A starter motor is an electric motor that drives the engine ___ when starting.

_____ **37.** A(n) ___ clutch is an engine component that allows slippage to prevent damage to the pinion gear during a misfire or unexpected reverse rotation.

_____ **38.** A(n) ___ is a sectional piece of copper that is directly connected to many loops of copper wire in contact with brushes.

T   F **39.** A 120 V starter motor operates similar to a 12 V starter motor.

T   F **40.** The flywheel ring gear is the gear attached to the engine flywheel driven by the pinion gear during engine starting.

T   F **41.** A normally closed switch interrupts current flow in the normal condition.

_____ **42.** A(n) ___ switch is usually used to operate an electric clutch that drives a mower deck or other main attachment of the piece of equipment.
- A. ignition
- B. power takeoff (PTO)
- C. operator presence control
- D. rotary ignition

_____ **43.** Testing multiple-pole, multiple-throw switches are typically referred to as "___" the switch.

_____ **44.** A switch ___ is the number of movable contact positions in a multiple-position switch.
- A. pole
- B. position
- C. spade
- D. throw

T   F   **45.** A proper functioning normally open switch will cause a continuity tester to emit an audible sound when tested for continuity.

T   F   **46.** Because PTO switches are usually designed to handle slightly larger-current loads, some circuit designers allow the operating current for the clutch to run directly through the switch.

_____ **47.** Using a(n) ___ allows a technician to compare expected results with actual test results to determine if a switch is functioning properly.

_____ **48.** ___ is the initiation of physical movement of the switch component used to change the switch operation.

T   F   **49.** Most switches used with outdoor power equipment have some type of alphanumeric identification for each spade connector on the switch.

T   F   **50.** When testing switches, a technician always tests for voltage, amperage, and resistance.

AC Voltage

_____ **1.** ___ is shown at B.

_____ **2.** The ___ pulse is shown at F.

_____ **3.** The peak ___ value is shown at A.

_____ **4.** The peak ___ value is shown at D.

_____ **5.** The negative ___ is shown at C.

_____ **6.** One ___ is shown at E.

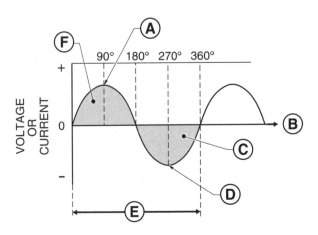

Starter Motor

_____ **1.** The ___ is shown at K.

_____ **2.** The ___ is shown at O.

_____ **3.** The ___ is shown at N.

_____ **4.** The ___ is shown at F.

_____ **5.** The ___ is shown at E.

_____ **6.** The ___ is shown at A.

_____ **7.** The ___ is shown at C.

_____ **8.** The ___ is shown at B.

_____ **9.** The ___ is shown at H.

_____ **10.** The ___ is shown at L.

_____ **11.** The ___ is shown at P.

_____ **12.** The ___ is shown at J.

_____ **13.** The ___ is shown at G.

_____ **14.** The ___ is shown at D.

_____ **15.** The ___ are shown at I.

_____ **16.** The ___ are shown at M.

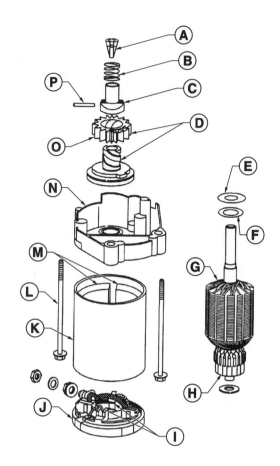

Current

_____ **1.** AC current is shown at ___.

_____ **2.** DC current is shown at ___.

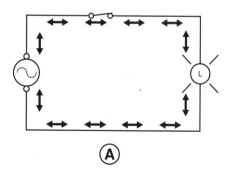

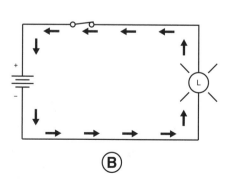

Name   Date

---

1. What type of DC current does a Briggs & Stratton 16 A alternator system provide to charge the battery?

    A. DC regulated

    B. DC unregulated

    C. DC regulated and unregulated

    D. none of the above

---

2. All Briggs & Stratton two-cylinder engines use a single ignition armature with two spark plug wires.

    True
    False

---

3. A zener diode needs a minimum of 12 V in the battery in order to function correctly.

    True
    False

---

4. As an alternator system is operating, the moving magnetic field under the flywheel induces voltage and current in the stator windings. If the charging system circuit is complete, current flows to various components including the battery. If the circuit is not complete, which of the following statements is correct?

    A. The alternator will have no current output.

    B. Voltage will be induced in the stator windings.

    C. No charging system components will receive any current.

    D. all of the above

---

5. The basic component that turns AC current into DO current to charge the battery is the:

    A. Alternator

    B. Battery

    C. Thermocouple

    D. Diode 61

6. Briggs & Stratton defines amperes as the amount or volume of electrons flowing past a specific point in a conductor per unit of time.

  True
  False

7. If the headlamps on a lawn tractor are part of a series circuit, which statement is NOT correct?

  A. If the filament in one headlamp burns out, the other lamp will not work.
  B. Both headlamps will be on at all times when the engine is running.
  C. There is only one return path to ground in this circuit.
  D. The total current in the circuit will flow through each of the headlamps.

8. Voltage is best described as the pressure or push within a circuit.

  True
  False

9. The purpose of the secondary winding in an ignition system is:

  A. On collapse of the primary field, the lines of magnetic flux pass through the secondary windings, inducing high voltage to jump the gap at the spark plug.
  B. The breaker points of the transducer cut the connection between the primary and secondary windings.
  C. The secondary windings are a backup to the primary windings, which provides reliability and recovery time between ignition pulses.
  D. A 60:1 winding ratio builds amperage to a level sufficient to jump the gap at the spark plug.

10. A break-away clutch is an electric starting system component that allows the starter motor to spin faster than the flywheel.

  True
  False

Name _____ Date _____

_____ 1. Heat flows whenever a(n) ___ difference exists in a material.

_____ 2. The direction of heat transfer is always from a ___ temperature to a ___ temperature.
   A. lower; higher
   B. lower; lower
   C. higher; lower
   D. higher; higher

_____ 3. In most cases, matter expands when ___.
   A. heated
   B. cooled
   C. heated or cooled
   D. none of the above

_____ 4. ___ expansion is the expansion of a material when it is subjected to heat.

_____ 5. On a liquid-cooled engine, the area of lowest temperature is the ___.

_____ 6. Thermal ___ is the increase in size of a material when heated with little or no change back to original dimensions.

_____ 7. ___ is heat transfer that occurs from atom to atom when molecules come in direct contact with each other, and through vibration, when kinetic energy is passed from atom to atom.

_____ 8. ___ is heat transfer that occurs as radiant energy without a material carrier.

_____ 9. Engine block material transfers heat by ___.

_____ 10. A(n) ___ is an engine component attached to the outer side of the flywheel that prevents harmful foreign matter from entering the path of cooling air to the engine.

_____ 11. Most Briggs & Stratton engines feature a(n) ___ cooling fan.

_____ 12. A cooling air ___ is a duct made from sheet metal, plastic, or similar materials that provides a specific path for the cooling air to enter the engine cooling system.

_____ 13. ___ is the period immediately following the initial shutdown of an engine when cooling air flow has stopped and the engine enclosure temperature increases for a brief time.

_____ 14. The cooling system in Briggs & Stratton liquid-cooled engines is pressurized to ___ psi – ___ psi.
   A. 8; 11
   B. 11; 13
   C. 8; 13
   D. none of the above

71

T F   **15.** A liquid-cooled engine cooling system continuously circulates coolant throughout the engine.

T F   **16.** A radiator is a multi-channeled container that allows air to pass around the channels to remove heat from the liquid within.

T F   **17.** Asperities are tiny projections from the machining process which produce surface roughness or unevenness.

T F   **18.** At atmospheric pressure, the maximum temperature that water can reach is 212°F before changing state.

_____ **19.** A(n) ___ is an engine component that moves coolant through passages of a liquid cooling system.

_____ **20.** ___ is the resistance to motion that occurs when two surfaces slide against each other.

_____ **21.** The SAE ___ rating is a number based on the volume of a base oil that flows through a specific orifice at a specified temperature, atmospheric pressure, and time period.

_____ **22.** A(n) ___ oil is an oil that has the characteristics of two viscosity ratings for the required flow at low ambient temperatures and has adequate oil film protection at high operating and/or ambient temperatures.

T F   **23.** Air-cooled small engines operate cooler than liquid-cooled or automobile engines.

T F   **24.** Briggs & Stratton recommends SAE 10W-30 multi-viscosity oil when the ambient temperature is below 40°F.

_____ **25.** A(n) ___ lubrication system is an engine lubrication system in which oil is directed to moving parts by a splashing motion.

_____ **26.** A(n) ___ is a splash lubrication system component used on vertical crankshaft engines consisting of a spinning gear with multiple paddles cast into the plastic gear body.

_____ **27.** A(n) ___ engine is an air-cooled engine in which cooling air flow routing and rate are controlled by air guides and a sealed blower housing.

_____ **28.** The ___ is a series of interconnected cavities cast into the engine block and cylinder head for the circulation of coolant.

_____ **29.** The letter "___" indicates an oil suitable for gasoline engines.

_____ **30.** A pressure ___ system is an engine lubrication system in which a pump is used to circulate oil in a limited area of the engine.

_____ **31.** ___ contains anticorrosive chemicals, lubricating components, and antifoaming agents.

T F   **32.** Heat always flows from an area of lower temperature to an area of higher temperature.

T F   **33.** Cast aluminum alloy engines and components have a higher degree of heat absorption than those made from cast iron alloy.

_____ **34.** A(n) ___ cooling fan has blades spaced at different distances from each other.

_____ **35.** ___ is a mixture of water and antifreeze used in liquid-cooled engines that is circulated throughout the engine cylinder block and other engine components.

Water Pump

_____ 1. The drive belt is shown at ___.

_____ 2. Cooled coolant is shown at ___.

_____ 3. The radiator is shown at ___.

_____ 4. The crankshaft pulley is shown at ___.

_____ 5. The crankshaft is shown at ___.

_____ 6. The water pump is shown at ___.

_____ 7. The radiator cooling fan is shown at ___.

_____ 8. The water jacket is shown at ___.

_____ 9. The bearing is shown at ___.

_____ 10. The cooling fan pulley is shown at ___.

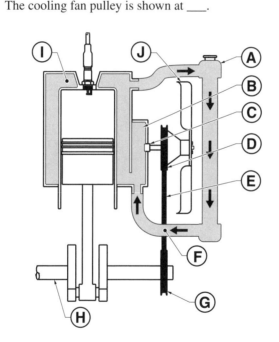

Cast Iron Alloy

Place a D in the space for each desirable property. Place a U in the space for each undesirable property.

_____ 1. Has structural integrity when mechanically or thermally stressed.

_____ 2. Has a porous surface providing small oil reservoirs.

_____ 3. Difficult to machine.

_____ 4. Has a high propensity for oxidation/corrosion.

_____ 5. Has reduced dimensional changes when placed under thermal stress.

API Certification Mark

_____ **1.** The administrating organization is shown at ___.

_____ **2.** The statement that all certification requirements are met is shown at ___.

_____ **3.** The specific application is shown at ___.

Liquid-Cooled Engine Cooling System

_____ **1.** The radiator is shown at ___.

_____ **2.** The radiator cooling fan is shown at ___.

_____ **3.** The thermostat is shown at ___.

_____ **4.** The cylinder head is shown at ___.

_____ **5.** The engine block is shown at ___.

_____ **6.** The water jackets are shown at ___.

_____ **7.** The water pump is shown at ___.

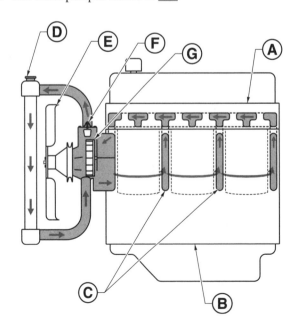

TEST 2
COOLING AND LUBRICATION SYSTEMS

CHAPTER 8

Name _____   Date _____

_____ **1.** ___ energy is the sum of all energy in a substance, including potential and kinetic energy.

_____ **2.** Small engines are commonly manufactured from cast ___ alloy.
   A. iron
   B. aluminum
   C. iron or aluminum
   D. none of the above

_____ **3.** On an air-cooled engine, the area of lowest temperature is the ___.
   A. fuel pump
   B. carburetor
   C. cooling fins
   D. cylinder head

_____ **4.** ___ conductivity is the ability of a material to conduct and transfer heat.

_____ **5.** The ___ of thermal expansion is the unit change in dimension of a material by changing the temperature 1°F.

_____ **6.** Thermal ___ is an asymmetrical or nonlinear thermal expansion of a material.

_____ **7.** ___ is heat transfer that occurs when heat is transferred by currents in a fluid.

_____ **8.** A(n) ___ engine is an engine that circulates air around the cylinder block and cylinder head to maintain the desired engine temperature.

_____ **9.** Cooling air circulating around the cylinder block and cylinder head transfers heat by ___.

_____ **10.** A cooling ___ is an engine component that supplies cooling air to the engine when rotated.

_____ **11.** A(n) ___ is a sheet metal or composite material component that encompasses the fan to direct cooling air to the cylinder block and cylinder head.

_____ **12.** Typically, the cross-section of the cooling air plenum should be at least ___ sq in. for each cu in. of engine displacement.

_____ **13.** A(n) ___-cooled engine is an engine that circulates coolant through cavities in the cylinder block and cylinder head to maintain desired engine temperature.

_____ **14.** ___ is an ethylene glycol chemical mixture used with water to lower the freezing point of engine coolant.

T   F   **15.** A pressurized cooling system produces a pressure lower than atmospheric pressure.

T   F   **16.** The first radiator was invented in the 1920s.

T   F   **17.** Lubrication of an engine helps to maintain proper operation by reducing friction and cooling internal engine components.

T   F   **18.** Oil film thickness increases with an increase in oil temperature.

_____ **19.** A(n) ___ is a valve placed between the radiator and the engine block on liquid-cooled engines that regulates the flow of coolant.

_____ **20.** ___ is the internal resistance to flow of a fluid.

_____ **21.** The viscosity rating number or weight for use in internal combustion engines ranges from SAE 10 to SAE ___.

_____ **22.** A(n) ___ is a molecule consisting of repeating structural units that have been chemically formulated to perform in a specific manner.

T   F   **23.** Briggs & Stratton recommends SAE 30 for temperatures at or above 40°F.

T   F   **24.** Most small air-cooled engines operate with oil temperatures that can exceed 600°F.

_____ **25.** A(n) ___ is an engine component attached to the connecting rod which directs oil from the oil reservoir to bearing surfaces.

_____ **26.** A(n) ___ oil pump is an oil pump that consists of a multiple-lobed inner rotor meshing with an outer rotor to discharge oil under pressure.

_____ **27.** A(n) ___ engine is an air-cooled engine in which cooling air is provided by the blower housing and ambient air flow.

_____ **28.** A radiator ___ is a device that pulls or pushes cooling air through a radiator.

_____ **29.** The letter "___" indicates an oil suitable for diesel engines.

_____ **30.** A pressure ___ system is an engine lubrication system in which a pump is used as the primary component to circulate oil throughout the entire engine.

T   F   **31.** Mixing antifreeze with water in a ratio of 68:32 lowers the freezing temperature from the standard 32°F (0°F) to –34°F (–37°C).

_____ **32.** Once absorbed into the material, kinetic energy is no longer considered ___ and becomes internal energy.

_____ **33.** Heat transfer from the combustion gases to the cylinder wall and from the cylinder wall to the cooling medium occurs by ___.
    A. conduction
    B. convection
    C. radiation
    D. all of the above

T   F   **34.** Partially ducted engines provide more control of the cooling air than fully ducted engines.

_____ **35.** Normal operating temperatures of small engines vary with engine design and commonly range from ___°F to ___°F.
    A. 150; 175
    B. 175; 195
    C. 175; 200
    D. 185; 220

Recommended SAE Viscosity Grades

_____ **1.** SAE ___ is recommended for the temperature range at A.

_____ **2.** SAE ___ and ___ are recommended for the temperature range at B.

_____ **3.** SAE synthetic ___ and ___ are recommended for the temperature range at C.

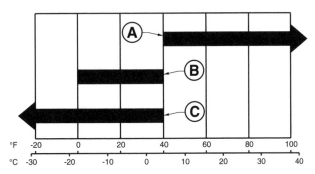

TEMPERATURE RANGE ANTICIPATED BEFORE NEXT OIL CHANGE

API Service Symbol

_____ **1.** A gasoline engine is noted at ___.

_____ **2.** The service category of this oil is shown at ___.

_____ **3.** The oil performance level is given at ___.

_____ **4.** The energy-conserving properties are given at ___.

_____ **5.** The SAE oil viscosity rating number is shown at ___.

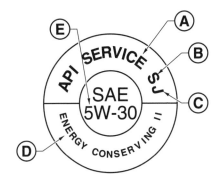

Combustion Gas Temperatures

_____ **1.** The intake event is shown at ___.

_____ **2.** The ignition event is shown at ___.

_____ **3.** The power event is shown at ___.

_____ **4.** The exhaust event is shown at ___.

_____ **5.** The compression event is shown at ___.

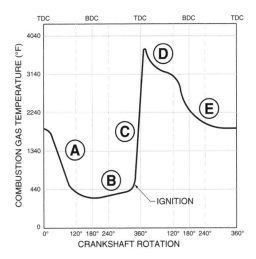

Radiator

_____ 1. Cooling air enters the radiator at ___.

_____ 2. Hot coolant from the engine enters the radiator at ___.

_____ 3. Coolant flows through coolant channels at ___.

_____ 4. Warmed air exits the radiator at ___.

_____ 5. Cool coolant exits the radiator to the engine at ___.

Oil Pressure

_____ 1. The inner rotor is shown at ___.

_____ 2. The outer rotor is shown at ___.

_____ 3. The dump orifice is shown at ___.

_____ 4. The check ball is shown at ___.

_____ 5. The oil pressure relief valve is shown at ___.

_____ 6. The spring is shown at ___.

_____ 7. The oil pump housing is shown at ___.

Engine Ducting

_____ 1. A fully-ducted engine is shown at ___.

_____ 2. A partially-ducted engine is shown at ___.

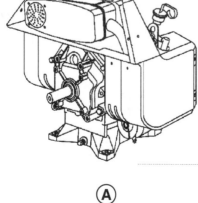

Ⓐ

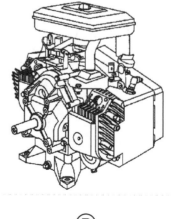

Ⓑ

1. Thermal growth is a heat-induced process causing a material to expand when heated with little or no return to its original size when cooled.

   True
   False

2. An engine equipped with a pressure filtration lubrication system has experienced a catastrophic failure. The gerotor oil pump is found to have a broken drive gear shaft. All of the bearing surfaces in the engine show signs of insufficient lubrication.

   Technician A says that the bearing surface failures throughout the engine are most likely caused by the failure of the oil pump.

   Technician B says that the oil pump failure did not contribute to the insufficient lubrication failure of the bearings.

   Which technician is correct?

   A. Technician A
   B. Technician B
   C. Both Technicians A and B
   D. Neither Technicians A nor B

3. Some engines are equipped with a float-style low oil level warning system that will shut the engine off if the oil level gets low. Which system or component does the system use to accomplish this?

   A. The fuel solenoid in the carburetor is energized when the oil is too low, which stops all fuel flow, causing the engine to stop running.
   B. The governor system forces the throttle plate to close completely, not allowing any air into the combustion chamber, causing the engine to stop running.
   C. The mechanical compression release system is actuated, lifting the exhaust valve off its seat causing a loss of compression, causing the engine to stop running.
   D. The primary circuit of the ignition system is directed to ground, causing the engine to stop running.

4. A rotating screen should always be installed in an application that is equipped with a cool air intake plenum.

   True
   False

5. The Vanguard™ three-cylinder liquid-cooled engine cooling system contains a thermostat in the engine block. Which of the following is not a function of the thermostat?

    A. Controls or regulates coolant temperature

    B. Provides quicker warm-up periods

    C. Builds pressure throughout the cooling system

    D. Maintains overall engine temperature through coolant flow control

6. A 50/50 mixture of antifreeze and water lowers the freezing point of the mixture while slightly lowering its boiling point.

    True
    False

7. When a cylinder is heated, the cylinder bore becomes smaller in diameter proportional to the amount of heat to which the cylinder is exposed.

    True
    False

8. A Vanguard™ three-cylinder liquid-cooled engine is losing coolant continuously. There is no sign of external leakage. The radiator needs to be refilled every eight hours of operation. An inspection shows that the radiator cap sealing washer is missing.

Technician A says that the missing seal on the radiator cap could account for the loss of coolant.

Technician B says that there is no sign of leakage around the radiator neck and that if the cap were the problem, the customer would see a puddle of coolant on the ground when the engine was operating.

Which technician is correct?

    A. Technician A

    B. Technician B

    C. Both Technicians A and B

    D. Neither Technicians A nor B

9. SAE 30 motor oil is recommended for use in all Briggs & Stratton engines that are operated in an ambient temperature of 32°F or higher.

    True
    False

10. A pressure filtration system provides oil pressure and volume to all bearing surfaces in the engine during operation.

    True
    False

Name _____ Date _____

_____ 1. A(n) ___-cylinder engine is an engine that contains more than one cylinder.

_____ 2. A(n) ___ engine is an engine that has two or more parallel cylinders adjoining each other.

_____ 3. Displacement is the volume that a piston displaces in an engine when it travels from ___ in the same piston stroke.
    A. TDC to BDC
    B. BDC to TDC
    C. all of the above
    D. none of the above

T   F   4. Multiple-cylinder engines produce more vibration during operation than single-cylinder engines.

T   F   5. Generally, the greater the displacement of the engine, the more power the engine can produce.

T   F   6. At peak production, Briggs & Stratton can manufacture 50,000 engines a day.

_____ 7. A(n) ___ carburetor is a carburetor that has a fuel reservoir located in the carburetor.

_____ 8. ___ is an engine condition that occurs when the engine continues to operate after the ignition switch is shut OFF.

_____ 9. Governor systems used for multiple-cylinder engines are usually ___.
    A. mechanical
    B. electronic
    C. mechanical or electronic
    D. none of the above

_____ 10. A(n) ___ is a magnetic pick-up located near the crankshaft pulley that senses and counts crankshaft rotation.

_____ 11. ___ load is any load applied to an engine that is over and above the frictional load of an engine.

_____ 12. ___ cycle is the length of time that equipment can operate continuously at its rated output within a given time period.

_____ 13. Multiple-cylinder gasoline or diesel engines are ___.
    A. air-cooled
    B. liquid-cooled
    C. air-cooled or liquid-cooled
    D. none of the above

_____ 14. A(n) ___ is a concave-shaped metal plug pressed into a hole at the water jacket used to provide a release for pressure from freezing coolant in a liquid-cooled engine.

_____ 15. A(n) ___ is a separate exhaust pipe used for each cylinder.

_____ 16. A(n) ___ is an electrically actuated component that controls the flow of fuel in the injection pump.

T   F 17. Gerotor oil pumps are commonly used on multiple-cylinder engines.

_____ 18. Diesel fuel is rated at approximately ___ Btu/gal.

T   F 19. Diesel engines require an electric spark to detonate the fuel.

T   F 20. A header pipe allows each cylinder to evacuate exhaust gases from the combustion chamber.

Liquid-Cooled Engines

_____ 1. The radiator cooling fan is shown at ___.

_____ 2. The water pump is shown at ___.

_____ 3. The radiator hose is shown at ___.

_____ 4. The radiator is shown at ___.

_____ 5. The thermostat housing is shown at ___.

Electronic Governor System

_____ 1. The governor linkage is shown at ___.

_____ 2. The carburetor is shown at ___.

_____ 3. The LAT motor is shown at ___.

_____ 4. The anti-afterfire solenoid is shown at ___.

_____ 5. The intake manifold is shown at ___.

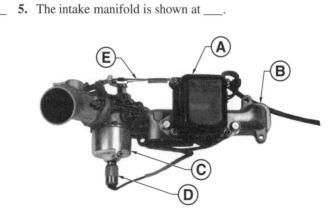

Name _____   Date _____

_____ 1. A(n) ___ engine is an engine that has two horizontal cylinders opposite each other.

_____ 2. A(n) ___ engine is an engine that has two cylinders forming a V-shaped angle at 60° to a horizontal plane.

_____ 3. When bore and stroke are known, the displacement of a multiple-cylinder engine is found by applying the formula ___.

A. $D = \dfrac{N}{0.7854 \times B^2 \times S}$

B. $D = \dfrac{N \times 0.7854}{B^2 \times S}$

C. $D = N \times 0.7854 \times B^2 \times S$

D. $D = \dfrac{1}{N \times 0.7854 \times B^2 \times S}$

T   F   4. Power strokes in multiple-cylinder engines occur more frequently, providing smoother operation.

T   F   5. Multiple-cylinder engine displacement is determined by multiplying the number of cylinders by the displacement of a single cylinder.

T   F   6. Fuel systems used for multiple-cylinder engines are exactly the same as those used for single-cylinder engines.

_____ 7. A(n) ___ is an engine component that distributes the air-fuel mixture from the carburetor to more than one cylinder.

_____ 8. A(n) ___ solenoid is a device that shuts OFF the fuel at the carburetor to prevent the engine from receiving fuel after the ignition switch is shut OFF.

_____ 9. The Vanguard™ three-cylinder engine can be equipped with a(n) ___ governor system.
A. mechanical
B. electronic
C. mechanical or electronic
D. none of the above

_____ 10. Most multiple-cylinder engines use a(n) ___ V electrical starter motor powered by a battery to start the engine.

_____ 11. A lawn mower blade is considered to be a(n) ___ load.

_____ 12. Duty cycle is expressed as a(n) ___.

_____ **13.** Air-cooled engines are ___ than liquid-cooled engines.
     A. more compact in size
     B. weigh less
     C. all of the above
     D. none of the above

_____ **14.** A(n) ___ is an engine component that collects and directs exhaust gases from each cylinder to the muffler.

_____ **15.** Diesel engines have a(n) ___ compression ratio than gasoline engines.

T   F   **16.** Pressure lubrication systems are commonly used on multiple-cylinder engines.

T   F   **17.** Multiple-cylinder diesel engines generally have a shorter life span than comparable gasoline engines.

_____ **18.** Gasoline is rated at approximately ___ Btu/gal.

T   F   **19.** The carburetor on a multiple-cylinder engine operates the same as a carburetor on a single-cylinder engine.

T   F   **20.** Diesel engines have traditionally been used as the power source for trucks, ships, and trains.

Automotive-Style Starter Motor

_____ **1.** The starter pinion gear is shown at ___.

_____ **2.** The drive housing is shown at ___.

_____ **3.** The drive lever is shown at ___.

_____ **4.** The bolts are shown at ___.

_____ **5.** The clutch is shown at ___.

_____ **6.** The end cap and bearing are shown at ___.

_____ **7.** The brush assembly is shown at ___.

_____ **8.** The brush springs are shown at ___.

_____ **9.** The starter housing is shown at ___.

_____ **10.** The solenoid is shown at ___.

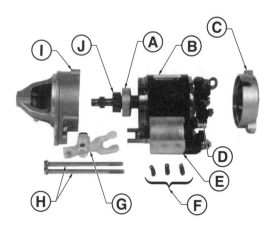

Compression Ignition Components

_____ **1.** The fuel lines are shown at ___.

_____ **2.** The injector is shown at ___.

_____ **3.** The injection pump is shown at ___.

_____ **4.** The fuel solenoid is shown at ___.

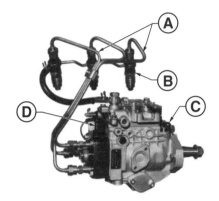

Compression System Components

_____ **1.** The valve train is shown at ___.

_____ **2.** The rocker arm is shown at ___.

_____ **3.** The crankshaft is shown at ___.

_____ **4.** The camshaft is shown at ___.

_____ **5.** The lifter is shown at ___.

_____ **6.** The piston is shown at ___.

_____ **7.** The valve is shown at ___.

_____ **8.** The counterweight is shown at ___.

_____ **9.** The connecting rod is shown at ___.

_____ **10.** The pushrod is shown at ___.

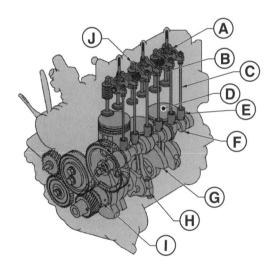

Diesel Engines

Place a D in the space for each diesel engine advantage. Place a G in the space for each gasoline engine advantage.

_____ **1.** Greater fuel economy

_____ **2.** Easier cold weather starting

_____ **3.** Longer life span

_____ **4.** Lower fuel volatility

_____ **5.** Lower engine noise

_____ **6.** Lower manufacturing costs

_____ **7.** Lighter engine components

_____ **8.** Lower exhaust gas emissions

Vanguard™ Three-Cylinder Engine Ignition System

_____ **1.** The battery is shown at ___.

_____ **2.** The ignition coils are shown at ___.

_____ **3.** The ignition module is shown at ___.

_____ **4.** The signal rotor is shown at ___.

_____ **5.** The trigger is shown at ___.

_____ **6.** The pick-up lug is shown at ___.

_____ **7.** The ignition switch is shown at ___.

MULTIPLE-CYLINDER ENGINES

Name _____ Date _____

1. The three-cylinder in-line Vanguard™ engine utilizes a common cylinder head to seal the combustion chambers of each cylinder. Which of the following statements is correct?

   A. The common cylinder head can affect the results of a cylinder leakdown test.

   B. The cooling system of this engine can affect any compression test performed on the engine.

   C. If the common head gasket is damaged, compression from one cylinder may leak into an adjoining cylinder.

   D. all of the above

2. When adjusting the valve stem to tappet clearance in a 180° opposed-twin engine, all valve springs must be installed to provide an accurate measurement.

   True
   False

3. The compression release system on a Vanguard™ V-Twin engine is unique. Why does this engine use two different pushrod materials?

   A. The steel pushrod is used because the engine dynamics cause increased loads on the intake valve spring.

   B. The aluminum pushrod reduces the temperature of the exhaust valve, significantly increasing engine life.

   C. The aluminum pushrod expands with the engine block, which allows the compression release system to remain operative despite increases in engine temperature.

   D. A steel pushrod provides increased durability under extreme load.

4. All Briggs & Stratton multiple-cylinder engines use a bowl-type carburetor.

   True
   False

5. The Vanguard™ V-Twin engine utilizes two diodes in the ignition armature wiring harness. If both diodes were to fail in the open position, which of the following symptoms would the engine exhibit?

   A. The engine would run on only one cylinder.

   B. The engine would have no spark.

   C. The engine would start and run correctly but would not shut off with the ignition switch in the off position.

   D. The engine would start and run correctly but would continue to run on one cylinder with the ignition switch in the off position.

6. The carburetor used on multiple-cylinder engines diners only slightly from the carburetor used on a single-cylinder engine.

    True
    False

7. The alternator used on the three-cylinder Vanguards engine is significantly different than the alternator systems used on most other Briggs & Stratton engines. Which of the following statements best describes the significant difference?

    A. The alternator uses single polarity magnets to induce current.

    B. The alternator uses a magnet to convert AC current to DC current.

    C. The alternator uses a field winding instead of a permanent magnet to induce current flow.

    D. all of the above

8. The governor spring location on the Vanguard™ V-Twin engine used in a generator application is in the governor arm hole farthest from the governor shaft.

    True
    False

9. Which of the following is NOT considered an advantage of diesel-powered engines compared to gasoline-powered engines?

    A. Greater fuel economy

    B. Longer engine life span

    C. Lower exhaust gas emissions

    D. Excellent cold weather starting

10. A freeze plug is a replaceable metal plug that is pressed into the water jacket of an engine and provides a release of pressure from freezing coolant.

    True
    False

Name _____ Date _____

_____ **1.** ___ is the systematic elimination of the various parts of a system or process to locate a malfunctioning part.

_____ **2.** A(n) ___ is the failure of a system, equipment, or part to operate as designed.

T   F   **3.** When troubleshooting, the small engine service technician never makes assumptions.

T   F   **4.** When troubleshooting, the small engine service technician isolates the cause of the problem as quickly as possible.

_____ **5.** The ___ method is a troubleshooting method that isolates the cause of a malfunction by splitting parts of a system in half until the cause is isolated.

_____ **6.** The ___ method is a troubleshooting method that isolates the cause of a malfunction by dividing the engine into separate systems and subsystems.

_____ **7.** The first step of troubleshooting is ___.
     A. isolation
     B. documentation
     C. investigation
     D. remedy

_____ **8.** ___ is the engine operation mode in which the engine cranks, the air-fuel mixture is drawn into the cylinder and compressed, and ignition occurs.

_____ **9.** ___ is the engine operation mode when the engine is shut down after operation.

_____ **10.** Before starting an engine during an inspection, the ___ should be checked.
     A. fluid levels
     B. guard positions
     C. loose parts
     D. all of the above

_____ **11.** A(n) ___ chart is a logical listing of problems and recommended actions.

_____ **12.** The ___ period is the period of time after the useful life of the engine when normal wear failures begin to occur.
     A. wear-out
     B. wear-down
     C. worn-down
     D. none of the above

T   F   **13.** Anti-afterfire solenoids are installed on engines that have a battery-powered electrical system.

T   F   **14.** Engine hunting and surging at true idle is caused by a fuel delivery problem or an air leak.

T   F   **15.** The carburetor was invented in 1925.

T   F   **16.** At true idle, the governor spring applies force on the throttle plate and has an effect on the idle characteristics of the engine.

_____   **17.** A(n) ___ leak is an undesirable discharge of gasoline which occurs when the engine is not operating.

_____   **18.** A battery ___ device is an electrical test tool that applies an electrical load to the battery while measuring amperage and voltage.

_____   **19.** A(n) ___ is an instrument used to measure the specific gravity of a liquid.

_____   **20.** A cylinder ___ test is a test that checks the sealing capability of compression components of a small engine using compressed air.

      A. leakdown
      B. leakout
      C. leaking
      D. none of the above

T   F   **21.** A DC amperage test is a test that uses a DMM to indicate the current that should enter the battery if all connections to the battery are good.

_____   **22.** The ___″ air gap in the spark tester simulates the minimum voltage requirements of an ignition armature under operating conditions.

_____   **23.** The coolant level should be no more than ___″ below the neck of the radiator fill hole when cool.

      A. ½
      B. 1
      C. 1½
      D. 2

T   F   **24.** Engine damage caused by an inadequate or excessive amount of oil is similar.

T   F   **25.** A minimum of 12,000 V is required to ignite the charge inside a typical combustion chamber.

DC Amperage Test

_____   **1.** The engine should be operating at ___ rpm for this test.

_____   **2.** The output connector lead from the stator or regulator-rectifier should be connected to the ___ test lead.

_____   **3.** The ___ test lead should be connected to the positive battery terminal.

_____   **4.** The DMM should be set to ___ current.

RED TEST LEAD

BLACK TEST LEAD

Name _____   Date _____

_____ 1. A(n) ___ is a sequence of operations that accomplishes desired results.

T   F   2. When troubleshooting, the small engine service technician works systematically.

T   F   3. When troubleshooting, the small engine service technician remedies only the effect of the problem.

_____ 4. The ___ method is a troubleshooting method that isolates the cause of a malfunction by grouping possible causes as easy, difficult, likely, and unlikely.

_____ 5. The ___ method is a troubleshooting method that isolates the cause of a malfunction by focusing on common problems identified by the manufacturer, product history, and/or service technician experience.

_____ 6. The ___ method is a troubleshooting method that isolates the cause of a malfunction by starting at one end of a system and progressing to the other end with sequential checks.

_____ 7. ___ skills are strategies and actions which allow a person to communicate effectively with other individuals in a variety of situations.
    A. Impersonal
    B. Interpersonal
    C. all of the above
    D. none of the above

_____ 8. ___ is the engine operation mode in which the engine has completed the startup mode and operates normally.

_____ 9. Over ___% of all gasoline sold in the United States contains ethanol.

_____ 10. A(n) ___ chart is a diagram that shows a logical sequence of steps for a given set of conditions.

_____ 11. ___ life is the period of time after the break-in period when most small engines operate as designed.

_____ 12. The ___ compression test is a test for engine compression in which the flywheel is spun counterclockwise and checked for the amount of rebound force.
    A. bounce back
    B. return
    C. turn around
    D. none of the above

T   F   13. Starting problems occur when the engine is cranking but does not operate.

T   F   14. Hunting is the desirable quick changing of engine rpm when set at a desired speed.

91

T   F   **15.** The first step in troubleshooting a fuel flow problem is to determine whether the problem is in the carburetor or the governor system.

_____ **16.** ___ hunting and surging is the undesirable quick and/or slow changing of engine rpm in a cyclical duration caused by excessive governor spring vibration.

_____ **17.** A(n) ___ leak is an undesirable discharge of gasoline which occurs when the engine is operating.

_____ **18.** ___ is a comparison of the mass of a given sample volume compared to an equal volume of water.

_____ **19.** A(n) ___ test is a test that uses a DMM to indicate the voltage potential of the alternator stator.

T   F   **20.** A resistive load is an applied load that reduces the possibility of the alternator system delivering full amperage through the circuit.

T   F   **21.** Cooling system problems are commonly caused by recirculation of hot exhaust gases and inadequate coolant flow.

_____ **22.** The ___ gap is the distance between the ignition armature pole and the secondary pole in the spark tester.

_____ **23.** The coolant should be flowing freely when the engine temperature reaches ___°F.
    A. 150
    B. 200
    C. 250
    D. none of the above

T   F   **24.** A spark tester is a test tool used to test the condition of the ignition system on a small engine.

T   F   **25.** High oil pressure cannot lead to external oil leaks.

Anti-Afterfire Solenoid Testing

_____ **1.** The plunger at ___ should retract when energized.

_____ **2.** The spade connector at ___ is connected to the positive terminal.

_____ **3.** A 9 V battery is shown at ___.

_____ **4.** The solenoid case at ___ is connected to the negative terminal.

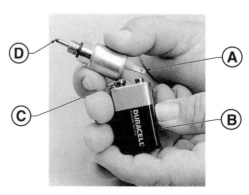

AC Voltage Test

_____ 1. The engine should be operating at ___ rpm for this test.

_____ 2. The output connector lead from the stator should be connected to the ___ test lead.

_____ 3. The ___ test lead should be connected to the engine ground.

_____ 4. The DMM should be set to ___.

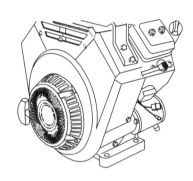

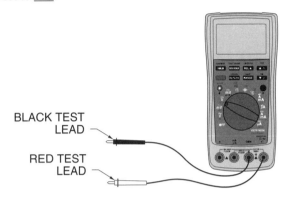

BLACK TEST
LEAD

RED TEST
LEAD

Flow Chart

_____ 1. The symbol at ___ indicates beginning or end.

_____ 2. The symbol at ___ contains a set of instructions.

_____ 3. The symbol at ___ contains questions.

_____ 4. The symbol at ___ indicates directions.

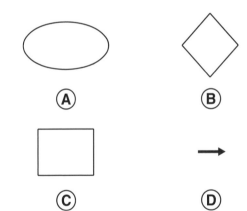

Ⓐ   Ⓑ

Ⓒ   Ⓓ

Engine Life Expectancy

_____ 1. The area at ___ indicates the useful life period of an engine.

_____ 2. The area at ___ indicates the break-in period of an engine.

_____ 3. The area at ___ indicates the wear-out period of an engine.

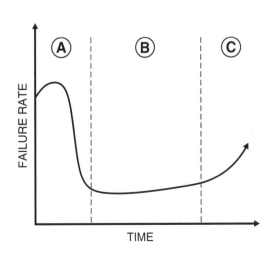

Ⓐ   Ⓑ   Ⓒ

FAILURE RATE

TIME

Split-Half Troubleshooting Method

_____ **1.** To measure voltage at the ignition switch, the ignition line must be disconnected at B and the red test lead connected at ___.

_____ **2.** To measure voltage at the ignition switch, the black test lead must be connected at ___.

_____ **3.** To measure voltage out of the starter solenoid, the red test lead must be connected at ___.

_____ **4.** To measure voltage out of the starter solenoid, the black test lead must be connected to ___.

_____ **5.** To isolate the problem to the starter solenoid, the red test lead must be connected at ___.

_____ **6.** To isolate the problem to the starter solenoid, the black test lead must be connected at ___.

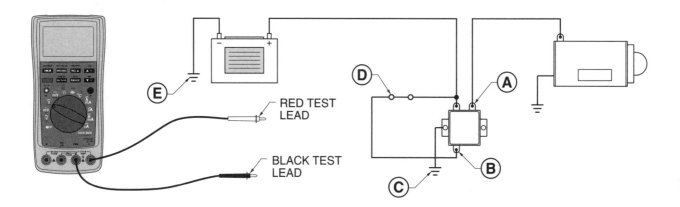

Name _____   Date _____

---

1. A static leak in a carburetor occurs after the engine has been sitting for several days. The carburetor does not leak during operation or any time soon after the engine is shut off and stored. This is most commonly caused by dirt in the fuel system.

   True
   False

---

2. A cylinder leakdown tester is attached to an engine and is prepared for the test. The air supply is not yet connected. Following the instructions for the tester, what is the next step in the testing process?

   A. Rotate the flywheel until the piston is at TDC between the compression stroke and the power stroke and lock the crankshaft in place.
   B. Attach the air supply, adjust the air pressure regulator to the setpoint, and lock the crankshaft.
   C. Attach the air supply, slowly rotate the engine to TDC between the compression stroke and the power stroke, and lock the crankshaft in place.
   D. Rotate the engine to TDC between the exhaust and intake stroke, lock the crankshaft into position, and attach the air supply.

---

3. An engine is received that hunts and surges at top no-load speed only. To determine whether the carburetor or the governor system is causing the symptom, a specific troubleshooting process can be followed.

   Technician A says that to separate the governor system from the carburetion system, place the speed control cable in the slow or idle position and manually snap the throttle linkage from idle to high speed several times. If the engine accelerates well, the governor can be eliminated as the cause of the symptom.

   Technician B says that to separate the governor system from the carburetion system, place the speed control cable in the slow or idle position and hold the throttle plate linkage against the idle speed screw with a finger. Slowly increase the engine speed using the idle speed adjustment screw until the engine reaches top no-load speed. If the engine does not hunt and surge, the problem is the governor system.

   Which technician is correct?

   A. Technician A
   B. Technician B
   C. Both Technicians A and B
   D. Neither Technicians A nor B

---

4. The specific gravity of battery electrolyte refers to the amount of weight the electrolyte adds to a dry cell battery.

   True
   False

---

5. When testing the output of a Briggs & Stratton alternator system, always test the AC circuit first if there is more than one test listed in the repair manual.

   True
   False

6. An engine is received with the customer complaint of "very hard to start when cold - runs well once started and warmed up."

   Technician A says that the most common reason for these symptoms is a misadjusted choke linkage or cable.

   Technician B says that this could be caused by a leaking exhaust valve allowing maverick air into the combustion chamber through the muffler.

   Which technician is correct?

   A. Technician A
   B. Technician B
   C. Both Technicians A and B
   D. Neither Technicians A nor B

7. An engine will not start. Upon inspection, a wet spark plug is found. The starting problem could be caused by:

   A. A leaking carburetor mounting gasket
   B. A stuck inlet needle
   C. Water in the fuel
   D. An open fuel shut-off valve

8. The ignition armature on a Magnetron® ignition system can be accurately tested for a heat-related problem using the Briggs & Stratton spark tester.

   True
   False

9. Sometimes, what appears to be a malfunction in the ignition system of an engine turns out to be an equipment-related cause. The engine and ignition system can be isolated from the equipment quickly minimizing the number of possible causes by:

   A. Removing the engine from the equipment
   B. Disconnecting the ignition armature ground wire at the stop switch or governor speed control bracket
   C. Disconnecting the blades, impellers, etc.
   D. none of the above

10. The compression rebound test is the most accurate and consistent method for testing the compression of a Briggs & Stratton engine.

    True
    False

Name _____   Date _____

_____   **1.** Engine ___ is the complete stoppage of the engine caused by the failure of one or more engine components.

_____   **2.** A head gasket leak in a liquid-cooled engine may result in ___.
    A. oil in the coolant
    B. coolant in the oil
    C. all of the above
    D. none of the above

_____   **3.** Abrasive ___ is a cause of engine failure through the undesirable introduction of abrasive particles into a small engine.

T   F   **4.** A diamond is harder than quartz.

_____   **5.** Air entering a typical Briggs & Stratton engine can reach speeds up to ___ mph.

_____   **6.** ___ air is undesirable, unaccounted air entering the engine through leaks caused by worn, loose, or failed engine components.

T   F   **7.** Troubleshooting is commonly performed on an operating engine.

T   F   **8.** Gasoline vapor in the carburetor exhibits some adhesive qualities.

T   F   **9.** The majority of wear from abrasive particles occurs at the bottom of the cylinder bore.

_____   **10.** ___ is the resistance to motion that occurs when two surfaces slide against each other.

_____   **11.** ___ friction is the force needed to accelerate or initiate the movement of a stationary mass.
    A. Static
    B. Kinetic
    C. all of the above
    D. none of the above

T   F   **12.** If one bearing surface contains scoring, the failure is caused by insufficient lubrication.

T   F   **13.** Up to 50% of the contents of a container of oil consists of oil additives.

_____   **14.** ___ is the accumulation of a semisolid, highly viscous oil material found in the crankcase of some internal combustion engines.

_____   **15.** A(n) ___ head gasket is an undesirable degradation of the head gasket which allows leakage to and from areas of the combustion chamber.

T   F   **16.** Engine failures caused by an excessive-oil condition are similar to those caused by a low-oil condition.

_____ **17.** In engines equipped with a governor gear and the proper crankcase oil level, approximately ___ of the circumference of the governor gear is located above the oil surface.
     A. ⅕
     B. ¼
     C. ⅓
     D. ½

_____ **18.** When an engine is shut OFF, it eventually cools to ___ temperature.

_____ **19.** A(n) ___ is a discoloration of the cylinder bore surface caused by an improper piston ring seal in a distorted cylinder block.

_____ **20.** ___ is a cause of engine failure from damage resulting from excessive engine rpm.

_____ **21.** A connecting rod commonly breaks at the thinnest part of the beam, approximately ___″ from the piston pin on most connecting rods.
     A. ½
     B. 1
     C. 1½
     D. 2

T   F   **22.** Abrasive particles that cause excessive wear in small engines commonly average 25μm or larger.

T   F   **23.** Most breakage engine failures are directly caused by or intensified by vibration.

T   F   **24.** Excessive heat can cause valve guide failures from a decrease in working clearance between the moving valve and the stationary guide.

_____ **25.** ___ wear is premature wear caused by abrasive particles which remove material from engine components through friction.

Low-Oil Conditions

_____ **1.** Scratching on engine component.   **A.** Galling

_____ **2.** Joining of engine components caused by heat, pressure, and/or friction.   **B.** Seizure

     C. Scoring

_____ **3.** Deep cut in an engine component caused by metal-to-metal contact, force, and motion.

Name _____   Date _____

_____ **1.** ___ is the systematic elimination of the various parts of a system or process to locate a malfunctioning component.

_____ **2.** A(n) ___ pattern is a uniform circular signature wear pattern on the intake valve face caused by abrasive particles.
  A. depression
  B. impression
  C. concave
  D. convex

_____ **3.** An abrasive ___ has enough hardness to cause the grinding or wearing away of material through friction.

T   F   **4.** Quartz is harder than topaz.

_____ **5.** A(n) ___ wear pattern is an area impacted by abrasive particles having specific appearance and dimensional characteristics.

_____ **6.** The intake valve ___ is the portion of the engine that provides a path from the carburetor or intake manifold to the intake valve head.

T   F   **7.** Silica is a compound of the elements silicon and nitrogen.

T   F   **8.** The first sign of abrasive ingestion in the cylinder bore is the premature loss of the cross-hatched pattern.

_____ **9.** ___ lubrication is a cause of engine failure from the absence, loss, or degradation of the oil film between two bearing surfaces.

_____ **10.** ___ friction is the friction exhibited by a moving mass.
  A. Static
  B. Kinetic
  C. all of the above
  D. none of the above

T   F   **11.** Oil is an incompressible liquid that has the ability to separate moving parts.

T   F   **12.** Most scoring occurs in the presence of some lubricating oil.

_____ **13.** Oil ___ is the deterioration of oil and its viscosity through oxidation, heat, and the accumulation of solids over time.

_____ **14.** ___ is a cause of engine failure from an engine component material that has distorted beyond a specific yield point.

T   F   **15.** The most common effect of overheating is a blown head gasket.

T   F   **16.** The main problem caused with an excessive-oil condition is the probability of air in the crankcase mixing with engine oil.

_____ **17.** Evidence of engine overheating is ___.
    A. almost always an effect
    B. not a cause
    C. all of the above
    D. none of the above

_____ **18.** Cylinder bore ___ is an engine condition caused by excessive temperature variations in the combustion chamber and the inability to adequately cool a portion of the cylinder bore.

_____ **19.** All exhaust valve seat inserts in Briggs & Stratton engines are installed with a(n) ___ fit into a machined hole.

_____ **20.** Each 500 rpm increase above the recommended maximum engine speed increases the maximum force on the ends of a connecting rod by ___%.
    A. 24
    B. 34
    C. 44
    D. 54

T   F   **21.** Any abrasive particle greater in size than the thickness of the oil film can cause damage to engine components.

T   F   **22.** In an overspeeding engine, a connecting rod almost always breaks when changing direction from BDC to TDC.

T   F   **23.** A liquid-cooled engine produces less overall noise than an air-cooled engine.

_____ **24.** A(n) ___ engine failure is an engine failure caused by more than one cause resulting in engine failure.

_____ **25.** ___ wear is premature wear from insufficient lubrication caused by an inadequate oil film to prevent undesirable wear from metal-to-metal contact.

Boundary Lubrication

_____ **1.** The cylinder wall is shown at ___.

_____ **2.** Boundary lubrication is shown at ___.

_____ **3.** The piston at TDC is shown at ___.

_____ **4.** The compression ring is shown at ___.

Name _____   Date _____

1. Two common causes of worn exhaust valve seats are an accumulation of carbon on the valve face and valve clearance set too wide.

   True
   False

2. A cause of insufficient lubrication could be:

   A. Seizure
   B. Scoring of the crankpin journals
   C. Excessive oil level
   D. none of the above

3. Hot spots found on a cylinder bore near the exhaust valve indicate that the engine has experienced some localized overheating.

   Technician A says that all hot spots are burnt oil on the cylinder bore and are of little concern as long as the cylinder bore is measured and found to be within specifications.

   Technician B says that the hot spots are signs of cylinder bore damage and should be repaired through a residing process.

   Which technician is correct?

   A. Technician A
   B. Technician B
   C. Both Technicians A and B
   D. Neither Technicians A nor B

4. An inadequate oil film between moving parts can result in scoring or metal transfer between the two surfaces.

   True
   False

5. An engine vibrates excessively during operation. A probable cause could be:

   A. A worn main fixed orifice jet
   B. Water in the fuel
   C. Loose mounting bolts
   D. none of the above

6. An effect of insufficient lubrication is:

    A. Seizure

    B. Breakage of internal components

    C. Scored bearing surfaces

    D. all of the above

7. Throttle shaft and bushing wear is caused by dirt sticking to the outside casting of the carburetor.

    True
    False

8. The signature wear pattern for abrasive ingestion in the crankcase is a satin gray dull finish on all aluminunn bearing surfaces.

    True
    False

9. An engine exhibiting obvious signs of abrasive ingestion is being analyzed. The cylinder bore is measured and found to be out of specification. The bore is much larger in diameter near the cylinder head compared to the bore measurement nearest the crankshaft. This pattern of wear indicates that the abrasives entered the engine through:

    A. The intake system

    B. The crankcase oil fill

    C. The crankcase breather

    D. none of the above

10. Discoloration is always found on scored bearings resulting from insufficient lubrication.

    True
    False

Name _____   Date _____

_____ **1.** ___ is the process of replacing the original engine on a piece of equipment with another engine.

_____ **2.** A(n) ___ replacement engine is a replacement engine that has the operating characteristics and required features of the original engine but is not supplied by the OEM.

_____ **3.** An engine ___ is the vertical, horizontal, and peripheral clearance space required for engine installation.

_____ **4.** The formula used to find the horsepower required for an electric generator is ___.

$$A. \ HP = kW \times \frac{1.34}{E}$$

$$B. \ HP = \frac{kW}{E} \times 1.34$$

$$C. \ HP = kW \times \frac{E}{1.34}$$

$$D. \ HP = \frac{E}{kW} \times 1.34$$

_____ **5.** A recommended maximum operating BHP curve is a graphic representation that indicates engine power at ___% of maximum BHP.
A. 70
B. 80
C. 85
D. 90

_____ **6.** A(n) ___ curve is a graphic representation that indicates maximum engine torque produced at a specific rpm.

T   F   **7.** A power curve represents the absolute maximum power that a particular engine can develop at the rated speed.

T   F   **8.** The governor droop for a walk-behind lawn mower is greater than the governor droop for an electric generator to allow for a wider range of engine rpm variation from load.

_____ **9.** A(n) ___ curve is a combination of rpm decrease and maximum brake horsepower (BHP) curves.

_____ **10.** A(n) ___ speed control is a control mounted on the engine that uses a speed adjustment nut to maintain an engine at a specific top no-load speed.

_____ **11.** A(n) ___ speed control is a control mounted on the engine that uses a friction lever to maintain an engine at a specific top no-load speed.

_____ **12.** A(n) ___ is an engine component fitted with baffles and plates that subdues noise produced from exhaust gases exiting the combustion chamber.

_____ **13.** ___ is the number of vibrations per second a noise contains measured in hertz (Hz).

    T   F **14.** The lowest engagement speed for a centrifugal clutch should be 3200 rpm to prevent accidental clutch engagement when the engine is started.

    T   F **15.** Adjustable fixed speed controls are commonly used on generators, pumps, and air compressors.

_____ **16.** ___ is damage that occurs to machine parts where two contacting surfaces are subject to slippage.

_____ **17.** A(n) ___ load is a load applied parallel to the shaft.

_____ **18.** A(n) ___ fan is an engine component mounted on the flywheel side of the engine that consists of a hub with bosses and tapped holes for connecting driven equipment components.

_____ **19.** A(n) ___ flywheel is a flywheel designed to provide the minimum engine inertia required independent of the external parasitic load.

_____ **20.** Engine horsepower decreases by ___% for each ___°F above 60°.
    A. 1; 5
    B. 2; 5
    C. 1; 10
    D. 2; 10

_____ **21.** The standard angle of operation limit for most small engines is a constant ___° angle under normal operation.
    A. 10
    B. 15
    C. 20
    D. none of the above

_____ **22.** Generally, No. ___ wire is used for battery charging and headlight circuits.
    A. 14
    B. 16
    C. 18
    D. none of the above

_____ **23.** Cooling fins should be cleaned after every ___ hours of engine operation.
    A. 10
    B. 25
    C. 50
    D. 100

_____ **24.** ___ operating conditions are conditions present which affect engine performance.

_____ **25.** The maximum lift distance for a Briggs & Stratton fuel pump is ___″ for engines with rewind starters.
    A. 3
    B. 6
    C. 9
    D. 12

_____ **26.** A(n) ___μ or finer fuel filter should be used on engines equipped with a fuel pump.

_____ **27.** Safety specifications commonly require fuel-wetted hose to withstand a minimum pull-off force of ___ lb at the fuel line connections on the carburetor and fuel tank outlet fitting.

_____ **28.** ___ is the state of the vibration wave frequency being equal to the natural vibration wave frequency of the component.

T   F **29.** Tight connections on the crankshaft PTO are required to avoid rocking, fretting, and/or damage leading to failure.

_____ **30.** The fuel tank outlet for a gravity feed fuel system must be at least ___″ above the fuel inlet fitting of the carburetor to ensure proper and consistent fuel delivery.

T   F **31.** A shear pin is designed to fracture at a higher axial torque than a rigid PTO coupling.

_____ **32.** ___ is the percentage of the belt surface in contact with the pulley circumference in a belt drive system.

_____ **33.** Power taken from the booster fan generally should not exceed ___% of rated horse-power.
    A. 25
    B. 30
    C. 40
    D. 50

_____ **34.** A(n) ___ is a grooved rotating wheel with a belt around a portion of the circumference used for moving loads.

_____ **35.** ___ is a condition of slow longitudinal movement caused by external forces.
    A. Centripetal force
    B. Centrifugal force
    C. Creep
    D. Slip

T   F **36.** The component closest to the source of vibration in a small engine is the one that typically has the maximum deflection.

T   F **37.** Many OPE applications have both synchronous and asynchronous designs on the same piece of equipment.

_____ **38.** ___ is a condition that occurs in a belt drive system when a V-belt wraps around the diameter of a V-shaped pulley, causing the normally flat sides of the belt that contact the groove in the pulley to begin to bulge outward.

_____ **39.** A(n) ___ coupling is a PTO coupling that has thick-wall tubing with a center keyway that fits both mating shafts.

T   F **40.** V-belts contain fiber or steel reinforcement to provide tensile strength.

T   F **41.** A flexible belt drive uses a chain belt to transfer power between a drive and driven shaft.

_____ **42.** A(n) ___ is a force applied to a drive system that causes a sudden, high load to be placed on all drive system components at the same time.

T   F **43.** All small engines produce toxic gases and must be operated in a well-ventilated area.

_____ **44.** A(n) ___ is a component that provides protection for a pulley/belt combination to prevent accumulation of debris near a rotating unit and to act as a barrier to protect rotating members from outside objects.

_____ **45.** ___ is a condition that results from a belt being pulled or stretched.

CPSC Requirements

_____ **1.** A(n) ___ rope is shown at A.

_____ **2.** The minimum distance at B is ___".

_____ **3.** The ___ is shown at C.

_____ **4.** The rope ___ is shown at D.

_____ **5.** The ___ speed control is shown at E.

_____ **6.** The outer end of the ___ is shown at F.

Horsepower

_____ **1.** What is the horsepower required to drive a 2.5 kW welder?

_____ **2.** What is the horsepower required to drive a 1.75 kW water pump?

_____ **3.** What is the horsepower required to drive a 5 kW hydraulic pump?

_____ **4.** What is the horsepower required to drive a 5 kW generator?

APPLICATION EFFICIENCY CONVERSION FACTORS	
Application	**Efficiency Conversion Factor***
Hydraulic pump	80
Generator	70
Welder	70
Water pump	50
Trash pump	40

* in %

Fuel Line Routing

_____ **1.** Water may accumulate in the fuel line shown at ___.

_____ **2.** Vapors may accumulate in the fuel line shown at ___.

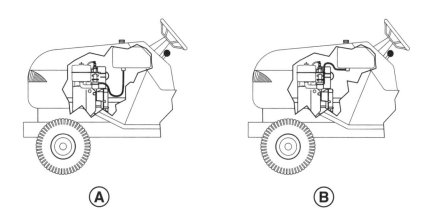

Power Curve

_____ **1.** The maximum BHP is shown by curve ___.

_____ **2.** The recommended maximum operating BHP is shown by curve ___.

_____ **3.** The torque is shown by curve ___.

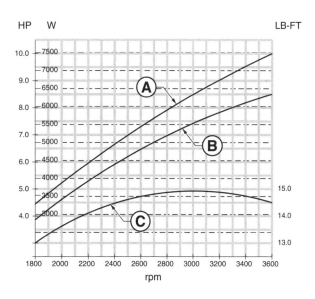

Speed Controls

_____ **1.** The speed control at ___ is an adjustable fixed speed control.

_____ **2.** The speed control at ___ is a remote speed control.

_____ **3.** The speed control at ___ is a manual friction speed control.

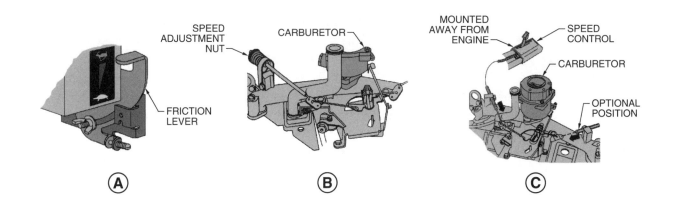

Engine Installations

_____ **1.** An open engine installation is shown at ___.

_____ **2.** A partial enclosure engine installation is shown at ___.

_____ **3.** A total enclosure engine installation is shown at ___.

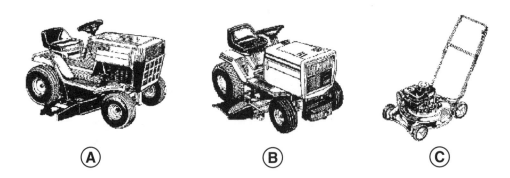

ENGINE APPLICATION AND SELECTION

Name _____ Date _____

---

1. What is the maximum radial load an engine equipped with plain aluminum main bearings can accept?

   A. 50 lb/sq in.

   B. 100 lb/sq in.

   C. 200 lb/sq in.

   D. 400 lb/sq in.

---

2. A small engine that produces 3000 W of power is a perfect match for a generator that produces 3 kW.

   True
   False

---

3. A power curve provides vital information when selecting an engine for repowering. Found on the power curve graph are two lines indicating horsepower.

   Technician A says that the maximum brake horsepower line is used to indicate the usable horsepower of any engine and should be consulted when selecting the engine.

   Technician B says the recommended brake horsepower line should be consulted when selecting an engine.

   Which technician is correct?

   A. Technician A

   B. Technician B

   C. Both Technicians A and B

   D. Neither Technicians A nor B

---

4. During an engine repowering evaluation on a commercial wide area walk-behind mower, which of the following would be an important exhaust system consideration?

   A. The exhaust deflector direction

   B. The location of the fuel line

   C. The location of the fuel pump

   D. all of the above

---

6. The recommended angle of operation for Briggs & Stratton engines is 15° or less from horizontal. Most engines will operate satisfactorily when operated at 30° intermittently.

   Technician A says that the angle of operation is mainly limited by the fuel delivery and carburetion system.

   Technician B says that the angle of operation is limited exclusively by the lubrication system.

   Which technician is correct?

   A. Technician A
   B. Technician B
   C. Both Technicians A and B
   D. Neither Technicians A nor B

7. The lowest engagement speed for a centrifugal clutch attached to a Briggs & Stratton engine should be 2200 rpm.

   True
   False

8. The PTO extension is always the portion of the crankshaft that sticks out beyond the crankcase of the engine.

   True
   False

9. An engine equipped with a single ball bearing on the PTO side of the crankshaft is applied to a water pump. The thrust load of the pump impeller must be:

   A. A maximum of 100 lb, away from the engine and away from the pump housing
   B. A maximum of 100 lb, toward the engine and away from the pump housing
   C. A maximum of 500 lb, toward the engine and away from the pump housing
   D. A maximum of 500 lb, away from the engine and toward the pump housing

10. The engine component farthest from the source of vibration (the engine) will usually exhibit the greatest deflection during operation.

    True
    False

FINAL EXAM

Name _____ Date _____

1. Small engines are generally rated up to ___ HP.
   A. 20
   B. 25
   C. 30
   D. none of the above

2. The maximum blade tip speed for rotary lawn equipment is ___ fpm.
   A. 14,000
   B. 19,000
   C. 23,500
   D. 25,000

T   F   3. The labeling on safety cans must comply with NFPA standards.

T   F   4. Piston rings are commonly made from cast iron.

5. Most walk-behind rotary lawn mowers use a ___ shaft, ___ cylinder engine.
   A. vertical; vertical
   B. horizontal; horizontal
   C. vertical; horizontal
   D. horizontal; vertical

6. The United States representative to ISO is ___.

7. Three methods of heat transfer are ___.
   A. conduction, convection, and locomotion
   B. conduction, radiation, and locomotion
   C. conduction, convection, and radiation
   D. none of the above

8. The atmospheric pressure at sea level is ___ psi.
   A. 0.147
   B. 1.47
   C. 14.7
   D. 147

T   F   9. The size of lawn tractor engines commonly ranges from 11 HP to 18 HP.

T   F   10. A compression ring is the piston ring located in the ring groove farthest from the piston head.

11. ___ is the point at which the piston is closest to the cylinder head.
    A. TDC
    B. BDC
    C. MDC
    D. none of the above

_____ **12.** Horsepower is a unit of power equal to ___.
   A. 746 W
   B. 33,000 lb-ft/min
   C. all of the above
   D. none of the above

_____ **13.** The compression ratio of most small engines ranges between ___ and ___.
   A. 5:1; 9:1
   B. 6:1; 8.5:1
   C. 5:1; 8.5:1
   D. 6:1; 9:1

_____ **14.** A(n) ___ is a narrowed portion of a tube.

_____ **15.** ___ is the ability of a fuel to resist engine knock and/or ping.

_____ **16.** Governor systems limit the amount of horsepower available by controlling engine ___.

_____ **17.** Water boils at ___°C.

_____ **18.** All Briggs & Stratton small engines use a ___° exhaust valve face angle.
   A. 37½
   B. 45
   C. 60
   D. none of the above

_____ **19.** The letter "___" indicates an oil suitable for gasoline engines.

_____ **20.** Small engines are commonly manufactured from cast ___ alloy.
   A. iron
   B. aluminum
   C. all of the above
   D. none of the above

_____ **21.** On four-stroke cycle engines, the camshaft rotates at ___ the speed of the crankshaft.
   A. ¼
   B. ½
   C. twice
   D. none of the above

_____ **22.** Most exhaust valves used in Briggs & Stratton engines are made from ___ steel.

_____ **23.** ___ is energy created by the flow of electrons in a conductor.

   T   F   **24.** A solenoid is a device that converts electrical energy into linear motion.

   T   F   **25.** Gerotor oil pumps are commonly used on multiple-cylinder engines.

_____ **26.** A(n) ___ is an instrument used to measure the specific gravity of a liquid.

_____ **27.** When an engine is shut OFF, it eventually cools to ___ temperature.

   T   F   **28.** A liquid-cooled engine produces less overall noise than an air-cooled engine.

_____ **29.** Generator applications require close control of the amount of governor droop to maintain ___ rpm under load.

_____ **30.** A(n) ___ load is a load applied parallel to the shaft.

_____ **31.** ___ life is the period of time after the break-in period when most small engines operate as designed.

_____ **32.** Resistance is ___.
  A. opposition to electron flow
  B. measured in ohms
  C. both A and B
  D. none of the above

_____ **33.** On a liquid-cooled engine, the area of lowest temperature is the ___.

T   F   **34.** Briggs & Stratton recommends SAE 30 for temperatures at or above 40°F.

T   F   **35.** A pressurized cooling system produces a pressure lower than atmospheric pressure.

Four-Stroke

_____ **1.** The stroke shown at A is the ___ stroke.

_____ **2.** The stroke shown at B is the ___ stroke.

_____ **3.** The stroke shown at C is the ___ stroke.

_____ **4.** The stroke shown at D is the ___ stroke.

Cooling System

_____ **1.** The cooling system at A is ___-cooled.

_____ **2.** The cooling system at B is ___-cooled.

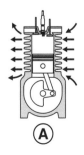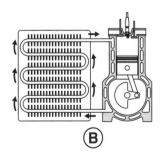

Combustion Gas Temperatures

_____ 1. The intake event is shown at ___.

_____ 2. The ignition event is shown at ___.

_____ 3. The power event is shown at ___.

_____ 4. The exhaust event is shown at ___.

_____ 5. The compression event is shown at ___.

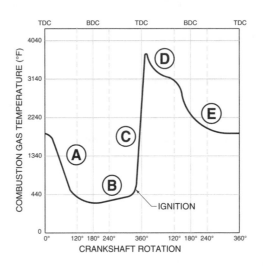

Detonation

_____ 1. Spark-induced ignition occurs at ___.

_____ 2. Combustion occurs at ___.

_____ 3. Detonation occurs at ___.

_____ 4. Knocking/pinging occurs at ___.

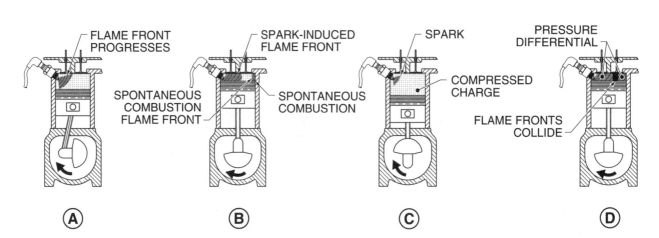

Compression System Components

_____ 1. The valve train is shown at ___.

_____ 2. The rocker arm is shown at ___.

_____ 3. The crankshaft is shown at ___.

_____ 4. The camshaft is shown at ___.

_____ 5. The lifter is shown at ___.

_____ 6. The piston is shown at ___.

_____ 7. The valve is shown at ___.

_____ 8. The counterweight is shown at ___.

_____ 9. The connecting rod is shown at ___.

_____ 10. The pushrod is shown at ___.

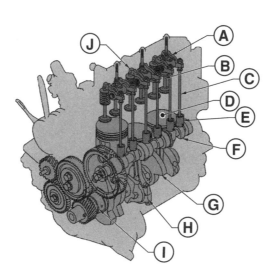